The Running Drug

How a running addiction helped one man overcome cancer,
conquer a marathon and rediscover life

Tim Beynon

Running is an individual sport, but I couldn't do it without my team.

This book is for Alex, William and Molly. Thank you for being my cheer squad.

Thank you for supporting Prostate Cancer UK

By buying this book, you have supported Prostate Cancer UK.

Twenty-five per cent of all book sales will be donated to the charity, so thank you for choosing to purchase this copy. One in eight men will contract prostate cancer in their lifetime, your donation will go a small way to helping support early detection in men and, I hope, to finding a cure for this awful disease.

To find out more about Prostate Cancer UK, visit www.prostatecanceruk.org

Contents

Prologue

I'm waving like a lunatic at a cameraman on a crane half a kilometre away, as are thousands of other people around me. We have all enviously watched this scene on TV for years, the iconic shot of the masses slowly shuffling their way down Blackheath Avenue in Greenwich, to the start line of the London Marathon. Today, however, we are the masses and the people at home are watching us.

We are held for a while in designated zones along the avenue, everyone anxiously wondering whether they should have gone for one final wee and hoping that they can get a GPS lock on their watches. When those at the front start to slowly move forward, the general hubbub increases and within a few seconds a multi-coloured array of clothing is thrown to the left and right of the road as runners discard the jumpers, bin bags and tracksuits they've brought with them to keep warm while they waited. Like being caught in a tornado, clothes fly everywhere, getting caught in trees and atop fences and occasionally hitting an unsuspecting marshal square in the face.

Next to me is a man in full cricket whites, with leg pads, helmet and bat - a GoPro mounted on its front - stretching and warming up like this is the most normal thing in the world. I ponder how many hours of training he must have undertaken in his full kit, running around a town somewhere, weekend after weekend, with puzzled locals wondering why he was in such a rush to get to a cricket match on a cold winter's morning. Here, however, he is just one of the masses, as are all those around me. Men, women, young and old, tall, short, fat, thin, the majority sporting a brightly coloured vest or t-shirt for one charity or another, several directly around me running with messages on their shirts, proudly displaying who they're running for and why.

It's one of the most surreal and emotional moments of my life. I haven't run a step yet, but I can already feel a lump in my throat and an almost overwhelming sense of accomplishment. For a while I struggle to make sense of why I'm feeling like this with the prospect of 26.2 miles still ahead of me and having done nothing more strenuous so far than walking the short distance from Maze Hill station.

Gradually, we move forward and as we round the corner at the end of Blackheath Avenue, stepping over more piles of discarded clothes and giving a final wave to the camera on the crane, the pack picks up the pace and we break into a gentle jog. A few yards ahead of me lies the start line and, as I cross the distinctive red timing mats that trigger the chip attached to the laces on my left trainer, it hits me. This is the moment I have been working towards for the past 16 months.

Introduction

There are days in our lives that ultimately define us. Our first step, our first day at school, our last day at school, our driving test, our first alcoholic drink, our first sexual dalliance, our wedding day, our first home, the birth of our children, the death of a loved one or the first time your son beats you at Fifa on the PS4. These are the life-defining moments that become imprinted on our psyches and change the course of our lives forever. Two such inextricably linked, but polar opposite moments happened to me just 16 months apart.

In December 2017, aged 40, I was diagnosed with stage two prostate cancer and in April 2019 I ran my first London Marathon. Two moments in my life, one possibly the lowest and one up there with the highest, uniquely challenging and uniquely emotional, but both symbiotically linked and genuinely life-changing in a whole host of unexpected ways. From the consultant's room to the finish line on The Mall, my cancer diagnosis, treatment and recovery became entwined in my bid to run the world's most famous and most popular marathon.

Prostate cancer kills more men in the UK than any other form of cancer. One in every eight men will be diagnosed with it at some point during their lifetime and 47,500 men in the UK receive this news every year. However, it is a disease that most men know little about, apart from the preconceived fact that a prostate exam involves a trip to the GP and a gloved finger. Often symptom-free, prostate cancer risk is increased for men over 50, black men and those with a family history, but if caught early it is both treatable and curable.

The London Marathon, meanwhile, has raised over a billion pounds for charitable causes since its inaugural race in 1981. Held in April (apart from those years blighted by a pandemic), across 26.2 miles of the Capital, it takes competitors past landmarks such as the Cutty Sark and Tower Bridge to its historic finish line in front of Buckingham Palace. Far more than a simple road race, it is an event that has come to reflect the power of the human spirit, with iconic moments including the sight of Matt Reeth helping the stumbling figure of Swansea Harrier runner David Wyeth down The Mall in 2017; 93-year-old Fauja Singh completing the race as its oldest ever finisher in 2004 and Simon Kindleysides becoming the first paralysed man to complete it, over 36 hours, in 2018. Having marked its 40th anniversary in 2020, the London Marathon remains the world's most popular long distance race, with 460,000 people applying for its ballot places each year.

The pages which follow therefore reflect on the journeys I have taken through both cancer and running, from my first faltering steps as an out of shape amateur to the finish line of the Marathon, via the doctors, tests, operations and tears that come with cancer. The training and taking part in one, has - as I hope you will see - helped me to come to terms with the physical and psychological impact of the other.

However, I am far from alone in having faced these dual challenges side-by-side. Thousands of runners with cancer, or recovering from it, have completed the London Marathon, each with a personal story of courage, determination, blisters and dodgy knees. Their stories are entirely unique, but all share a common thread, a love of running as a means to boost their physical and psychological wellbeing. They are the poster boys and girls for a sport that is booming in the UK and proven to support recovery, and they are the men and women who have raised millions of pounds for cancer charities, saving the lives of countless other patients across the country.

Running for them, as I have found for myself, is the wonder drug that can help you achieve the seemingly impossible. So, if you are reading this and are either coming to terms with your own cancer diagnosis, or beginning a journey to recovery, my message is simple: Stay strong, stay positive and keep running.

Chapter 1 - The sedentary years

I haven't always been a runner. In fact, for a large part of my life I have hated running and for other sizable chunks of it I have been utterly ambivalent to the concept of physical activity as a pastime. This ambivalence can otherwise be referred to as my childhood, adolescence and young adult life, in other words; that period of existence for which Mother Nature has designed our bodies to be at their physical peak.

The irony of this is not lost on me. Had I been born a few thousand years earlier, I would have spent these wilderness years in, well, the wilderness. Running to eat, running to survive and generally running everywhere, I would have been using my God-given gift of youth, fitness and strength to further humankind and pull myself up the evolutionary ladder. As it happens, I spent my wilderness years playing *Sonic The Hedgehog*.

At school in the depths of the Somerset countryside, my friends and I looked on running as a form of twice-weekly punishment disguised as physical education. Throughout the winter months, we were forced to run the universally disliked cross-country course, a two-mile circuit that our adolescent legs despised. It began with two humiliating laps of the rugby pitch - which would routinely reduce some of my weightier classmates to tears - and wound its way down narrow paths and across disgruntled farmers' land, including a gateway between two fields that was known simply as 'the bog.'

There was no easy way to cross this cow-trodden mud pit, it was around 10-metres in length, fringed by thorny hedgerows and waterlogged year-round. The sight of Matthew Watts rather feebly trying to extract his football boot from the bog - like a World War One Tommy struggling to extract his rifle from the fields of the Somme - has never left me. The bog became the stuff of legend, the site at which unlucky runners would either lose their footwear or their dignity. Approached with trepidation, the feeling of relief at safely crossing the obstacle without face planting in the oddly smelling (we always thought chicken excrement) filth and still sporting two, mud-covered boots was immense. Running the rest of the course with two pounds of countryside caked to each foot, however, only added to our overall loathing of cross country.

Our PE teachers, meanwhile, had a habit of appearing from behind a hedge whenever any of us dared to walk, barking encouragement in the form of harsh whistle blowing and such inspirational words as; "Beynon...move!" However, despite this boot camp approach to pastoral care, one nugget of running advice on a particularly cold cross-country session from one whistle-wielding teacher has always stuck with me. He shouted at me once to squeeze my thumbs when running to avoid a stitch and, to this day, I always have done.

While the winter months of my school years brought with them the humiliation of cross-country, the summer months saw the PE department dusting off the shot puts and chalking an irregular running track around the outside of the cricket pitch. Track and field, it has to be said, was a somewhat lackadaisical affair at my school. You could sense that the PE teachers didn't really share the same level of passion for the Olympic staples as they did for the more traditionally British sports of football and rugby. The standard of track and field instruction was a giveaway to this fact, as it was usually delivered as follows:

Javelin: "Pick it up and chuck it."
Shot put: "Pick it up and chuck it."
Discus: See above
Long jump: "Run, then jump."
High jump: "Run, then jump a bit higher."
100m, 200m: "Run as fast as you can."
400m: "Run as fast as you can and try not to die."
1,500m: "Just try to make it to the end."

Even at school, however, the sprint disciplines were the glamour events, especially on Sports Day. The 100-metres and the 200-metres evoked the loudest cheers, with the sportiest kids gaining legendary status and all claiming to have beaten a school record that had apparently stood for 30 years. The 800-metres and 1,500-metres, however, were a different kettle of fish.

9

The level of enthusiasm for middle distance races - amongst competitors, spectators and teachers alike - was on a par with that for double maths on a Friday afternoon. No one could be bothered, and no one was really interested. Those unlucky enough to be taking part in these multi-lap affairs were lucky if they got a lukewarm ripple of applause on the first lap, and stood no chance of even a thumbs up by the third. I am also certain now that the teachers - in their discussions over anything other than the athletics in front of them - abjectly failed to keep count of the number of times we'd pass them, randomly ringing a bell when they felt it was probably about time for the last lap. On reflection, in fact, I'm sure that the rather tired looking Darren Jennings actually probably ran a 10K when he took first place in the fourth years' 1,500-metre race in 1994. Well done Dazza, top effort mate.

After school, through sixth form and into my university years, exercise of all kinds became less and less frequent. While I recall the occasional game of squash with my housemates, the majority of energy exuded during my higher education was spent recovering from hangovers. It was not a healthy time. The standard of food consumed was poor and judged mainly on whether or not it could be microwaved in under five minutes. The amount of alcohol consumed was disproportionate to, well, everything and the amount of time spent in a seated or fully-reclined position equated to pretty much every waking hour.

I was the human equivalent of a scatter cushion for a number of years and spent more time thinking about bar snacks than I did about my overall fitness. Indeed, had someone suggested sticking on a pair of trainers and going for a run I would have been more concerned for their mental wellbeing than my own health.

This general lethargy continued into my 20s and my early working life as I made my way as a copywriter in the cut and thrust world of monthly special interest motoring magazines. This was an exciting time, I was earning money, I was living in London, I was going out, I was having fun, but I still wasn't doing any exercise. Indeed, I think it took until my mid-20s and the challenge of a friend to take part in a 10km race in central London, for me to even contemplate running for anything other than a bus.

Looking back on those years today, I cannot understand why I was so sedentary and why exercise wasn't on my radar. Yes, the proliferation of news wasn't as widespread back then, but I must still have been aware of the dangers of doing so little. Why didn't I listen to that and get off my arse?

I suppose the answer lies in the ignorance of youth. When we're young, we think we're invincible. We work hard (kind of), play hard, take risks and think little of the consequences. We do the crazy things that we will talk about in later life and advise our own children never to do. Scuba diving at night on the Barrier Reef with barely two days tuition, great fun at the time, but an utterly insane, 'what the hell was I thinking,' memory today. It's a wonderfully care-free time of our lives when thoughts of things like heart disease, diabetes and cancer are filed away, alongside mortgages and pensions, as something to worry about in 20 years' time.

However, there comes a time, eventually, when the reality of one's prior contempt for exercise hits home. For me, that came on the first training run I attempted for the aforementioned 10km challenge, although the ignorance of youth was still there, together with the cockiness:

"Ten kilometres, six miles...easy! I hardly need to even bother training. I could do that tomorrow. Take me to the park, point me in the right direction and I'll see you losers at the finish line. Let's say 40 minutes, sounds reasonable, not pushing it too hard. That's hardly more than an episode of *Neighbours* after all. Right then, bring it on!"

Oh dear.

Chapter 2 - Ten of the best

ands on knees, head between legs, retching. I was utterly spent, physically drained and incapable of stumbling another step. To the horrified passers-by on the Thames Pathway who were unsure whether or not to run for the nearest defibrillator, I must have looked like I had completed my first ultra-marathon in a world record time. Or, as was more likely, they were inwardly laughing at a 20-something couch potato who had spectacularly overestimated his physical fitness and was attempting something as alien to him as healthy eating and early nights.

This was the scene at the end of my first 10-minute 'training' run after accepting the challenge of a lifelong friend to join him for the inaugural *Nike Run London* 10km race in 2001. I was 24 and I had just discovered that I was in the worst shape of my life. For a start, It had taken me twice as long to get ready as it had to actually complete my first run. As for the experience itself, it had started well, but had gone rapidly downhill from about the second minute. I had walked the route, from the front door of my Battersea flat to the edge of Battersea Park countless times, but tackling it at speed was an entirely different experience. My first realisation - about a minute into the run - was that I hadn't actually run for anything for more than a minute, for years. Busses, trains, the very occasional football, badminton or tennis match, all required an element of running, but never continuously for more than about 30 seconds. Short, sharp runs I could handle, but with this I had to keep going and going and going. My legs complained bitterly, my heart tried to escape from my chest and my lungs gasped for air like I was climbing Everest.

My mental plan for that spring day in 2001 was to run from home, trot around Battersea Park and canter back again, skipping through the front door to impressed back slaps from my flat mates. The sad realisation that I had not even managed to make it to the park itself, however, gave me a sobering reality check and sent my youthful arrogance packing. Here I was, looking like I was having a heart attack on one of the most popular running routes in the Capital, while proper runners breezed past me, glancing down at my hunched, wheezing figure with looks of either contempt or pity. As epic fails go, this was right up there with Eric 'the eel' Moussambani's attempt to qualify for the 100m freestyle finals at the 2000 summer Olympics (Google him, it's brilliant). Indeed, very much like the swimmer from Equatorial Guinea - who had never seen an Olympic-sized swimming pool until he dived into it – I was clearly massively out of my depth.

At such a tender age, I wasn't used to being slapped down this hard so, after regaining my composure and while my entire body recovered from delayed onset muscle soreness (DOMS), I set about researching 10km training plans. Little did I know then that I was on the start of a journey that would one day see me cross the finishing line of the London Marathon, a prospect at the time that seemed about as achievable as my childhood ambition of winning the Formula One World Championship. Right then though, my goal was to get to the end of those 10 kilometres and, more importantly, not to be beaten too badly by my much fitter friend.

I found a plan and discovered a new word: fartlek. After stifling my inner seven-year-old's desire to snigger at the term, I was delighted to find that this new addition to my vocabulary meant that I could start my training by walking. Well, more accurately, running for a bit and then walking, and then running again. Thank God for the Swedes, first they gave us Abba, then meatballs and now this, the running equivalent of sitting in a traffic jam. It was the kind of training plan that I could embrace, simply because it included 50 percent less running than any other plan I had come across.

Over the coming few weeks I stuck to the plan religiously and very slowly saw my stamina and distance improving. I was getting into the park and making it back home without needing life support. This was progress. Of course, I had no real idea back then of how far I was actually running. I had no running watch, thought GPS was a parcel delivery service and owned a clamshell mobile phone that could barely make calls, let alone track my every step. So I remember using some basic online maps to try and work out how far I was going on each run and how I would need to extend them to get close to the 10km target I was aiming for. On reflection, it makes you appreciate how spoiled we are today with wearable technology making it so easy to measure every kilometre we run and every metre we climb. Today we can plan every run, to time and to distance, with confidence and it seems archaic to think that we once used to make it up as we went. Mind you, life was also a lot simpler when our post-run regimes simply involved a shower. Today, we sync, upload, name our runs, add photos, measure splits, track segments, assess pace versus elevation, monitor heart rate and give kudos to everyone we ran with or past, and then take a shower. It's exhausting!

But despite the old school route planning, the training went well and I found myself enjoying it. One run in particular has always stuck with me from those early days. It was the week before the *Run London* event and my friend Keith - who had laid down the challenge - and I set off for a run alongside the Thames. It was to be a familiar route, through Battersea Park, across Chelsea Bridge and returning via Albert Bridge. It was just a couple of miles, three at a push, but within a few minutes of leaving the comfort of my flat, the sky darkened in an almost biblical fashion. The heavens opened soon after and the rain fell in buckets, like something from the tropics. Regardless, we continued, ploughing through puddles on now empty paths as everyone else ran for cover. We couldn't get any wetter than we were, our clothes and trainers were soaked through, so continuing made no difference whatsoever. We flew across Albert Bridge Road and into Battersea Park.

Usually packed with dog walkers, meandering couples and children, the park was utterly deserted, its wide paths filling quickly with water to become shallow rivers and its trees swaying precariously in the gusty winds. Glancing at each other, we couldn't quite believe it, and then the first bolt of lightning lit up the sky, followed seconds later by a deafening clap of thunder. It was as if Mother Nature was challenging us to a duel. Would we dare to run on with the storm seemingly centred above our heads? Well, yes.

We had the whole park and London's streets to ourselves, it was our running playground for as long as the storm kept everyone else inside. I don't think I've ever run with more of a sense of liberation. We were David taking on Goliath for those few miles and I simply remember wanting to run and run, and for the storm to never end.

Ever since, I have never baulked from running in the rain, it is as close to nature as one can get and I would encourage everyone to embrace it. Don't put off a run if it looks a bit damp and don't put on extra layers, hats and gloves either. Your skin is all the waterproofing you need and, if you accept that you're going to get drenched, you won't notice it. Instead you'll experience the kind of freedom usually reserved exclusively for those appearing in shampoo adverts. It's a must for everyone who likes to run.

As for the *Run London* 10km, my first ever running race, I finished it in an hour and four minutes, and I was chuffed to bits. Well, chuffed to bits, and spectacularly frustrated that I had gone four minutes over the hour mark. Surely I could get under an hour. What would it take to shave those pesky four minutes off my time? Could I have run faster? Yes. Could I have trained more? Yes. There was only one thing for it.

I needed another race.

Chapter 3 - Falling in love

Running in a timed race, against others, is an eye opening experience. For everyone outside of the elite circle, there is absolutely no chance of winning, no chance of even making the top 10. Indeed, most of us go into each race knowing that we'll romp home somewhere between 205th and 4,096th place. There is no prize money and no fame - in fact, it has usually cost us a considerable amount of money to compete and no one other than our immediate circle of friends, often even knows we're there. So why do we do it?

As I found out back in 2001, we do it because we're driven by an unquenchable thirst to beat ourselves. Once a benchmark has been set - be it of time to complete a distance, or of total distance run - that benchmark has to be beaten. For me, my first race left me with a four-minute challenge that I was determined to overcome. No one else cared less, but I knew I could run 10km in under an hour, and I was determined to prove to myself that I could. I was in direct competition with my body.

This has to be a uniquely human trait, surely. I cannot imagine any other species on the planet being this hard on itself. I have yet to see a David Attenborough documentary in which the cheetah, having previously sprinted across the dusty savannah of Northern Africa at 72mph in pursuit of lunch, attempts it again a week later purely in order to hit the 73mph mark on the speed trap.

Running for the rest of the animal kingdom is about survival. It is a means to an end; lunch for the cheetah, or the chance of escape for the gazelle. For humans though, it is about personal challenge and individual sports like cycling, swimming and running, give us an outlet through which we can test our endurance and our capacity to improve. They also allow us to set our own goals and, as was reaffirmed for me when cancer came knocking on my door, they allow us to measure, test and boost both our physical and psychological wellbeing. But more on that later.

So it was that throughout the second half of my 20s and into my 30s, my goals with running were to improve and maintain a steady level of fitness and to enter the occasional race, ensuring that I beat my times on each occasion. I smashed the one hour 10K ceiling and subsequently set about chasing a sub-50 minute target - which remained elusive until my 40s. The 10K, meanwhile, became a staple distance, both in terms of training and racing. It was long enough to give me reassurance in maintaining a level of fitness that was at least above that of my non-running friends, and short enough to fit in perfectly around work, social life and TV schedules. With the exception of the Bristol Half Marathon in 2003 - an experience that once again proved hugely frustrating as I crossed the line in 2 hours and 10 minutes - this status quo held for the best part of a decade.

Ironically, it wasn't until my life became even more chaotic - with the arrival of my children, a house move and a job that saw me top and tail my daily commute with a six-mile bike ride - that the whole running thing became a bit more serious.

I was 33 and had managed to secure myself a job with Central YMCA, the world's first YMCA and home to the largest gym in Central London. It came with a frightening level of responsibility, but also with a free gym membership and an array of colleagues who were either part-time personal trainers, triathletes or sub-three hour marathon runners. The office exuded fitness. My role was to market the benefits of physical activity to the masses and, in an environment that lived and breathed exercise, the passion of those around me inevitably rubbed off.

Here I was, working for a company that loved exercise, with people for whom it was their reason for being and with access to state of the art fitness facilities. Despite feeling like an amateur when I first started the role, I soon found myself talking the talk and living the fitness life with my new uber-fit colleagues. The company also gave all those who used the gym an additional 10 minutes on their lunch break, so most lunchtimes involved some kind of activity in the gym or pool, or on the streets of central London.

Most of my immediate YMCA work colleagues were runners and an informal lunchtime running club saw us take to the streets of the Capital on various routes from Tottenham Court Road to Regent's Park and Primrose Hill. Dodging past pedestrians, weaving between traffic and racing to Primrose Hill in order to do a few hill reps before returning to the office became a regular part of our working week. I loved it and will remain forever grateful to those colleagues who took it upon themselves to push me through assorted interval sessions and long runs during my time at the charity. They instilled a new passion for lunchtime and weekday running that has stayed with me ever since, ensuring that I ran more regularly in my 30s than I had ever done before.

I found that running with such regularity quickly becomes habit forming and, far from struggling to motivate oneself to get out of the front door, not running on the days you usually do becomes frustrating and evokes a sense of guilt. Missing a lunchtime run because of an over-running meeting, for instance, can see you developing an instant dislike for the meeting organiser. Planning one's own day around a lunchtime run, meanwhile, becomes par for the course.

And so it remained for the next seven years. Running had become ingrained in my daily routine and in my very existence, it was as important to me as eating and sleeping and gradually took the place of drinking. Indeed, partly because of my unashamed reputation as a lightweight and partly down to the early morning commitments that come with parenting, running in my 30s became my outlet for frustration and stress, rather than late night drinking. Sore muscles replaced sore heads and, although I didn't go as far as cutting out booze altogether (I decided to save that until my 40s), I felt fitter, healthier and more alive than ever before.

Then I reached 40.

Chapter 4 - Turning 40

Forty; four-zero...the big four oh....however you spin it, for most of us entering our fourth decade is a big deal. It's the birthday that tradition dictates no one wants to reach. It's the birthday on which your cards switch from being witty and anecdotal to fixated on your pending senility. It's the birthday that apparently - according to one particularly depressing birthday card I received - marks the old age of your youth. So is it any surprise that all this rather depressing convention makes the occasion of one's 40th birthday about as eagerly anticipated as root canal surgery?

At least that's how convention would have you believe our 40th birthdays should be. For me, I just wasn't bothered. I headed into my big birthday with no anxiety whatsoever. It was just another year and at that point I was as far from a mid-life crisis as one could be. I had no desire to swap the family Vauxhall Zafira for an impractical sports car; I was happy to steer clear of lycra and road bikes; I had no interest in golf and I was perfectly content in my marriage, so had no need for a Swedish au pair. Forty held no fear for me and I looked forward to celebrating it with my family and friends in a low-key way with minimum fuss.

As it happens, I ended up making myself a Lemsip and going to bed early on my 40th as a bout of pleurisy - a Victorian-sounding, flu-like bug that leaves you with the mother of all coughs - wiped me out and meant that my birthday ended up being about as exciting as *Speed 2*. I managed to struggle my way through a pre-planned camping trip with some friends a few days later, but a course of antibiotics meant that I had to watch on with a mug of tea as they all drank the celebratory alcohol around the campfire.

In hindsight, however, I was secretly pleased not to have to go near the whisky my best man had brought to the occasion, especially judging by the collection of sore heads that greeted us the following morning. I am not well known for my drinking prowess and have a long history of spectacularly embarrassing myself after a surprisingly small amount of alcohol. From puking on a friend's mother's shoes - while she was wearing them - aged 17, to forgetting every moment of my stag do aged 32. I have always found alcohol to be that annoying friend who trips you up when you least expect it, the kind of 'friend' who pressures you into doing something stupid and then stands back and laughs as you dance to *Agadoo* on the table at your work Christmas party. So, skipping the hangover on that 40th camping trip and settling for a hacking cough and antibiotics was actually a birthday bonus in my eyes.

Today, I am tea total. I have been for the best part of a year and I don't miss alcohol in the slightest. However, I'm not going to sit here and pretend to be virtuous or preach to you about the life-changing enlightenment that comes from giving up booze, simply because there is no life-changing enlightenment. I just chose to stop and I stopped, that's it. I realised I didn't really like it, in much the same way as I realised I didn't really like horror movies. I had previously enjoyed both but, on reflection, eventually realised that each made me feel a little sick and neither added anything positive to my life. Non-alcoholic Pilsner and back-to-back episodes of the American version of *The Office*, meanwhile, well that's a different story altogether.

It may also sound spectacularly clichéd, but I have found that running has replaced the stress-busting high that alcohol once gave me. Gone are the days when I would reach for a beer after coming home from work, stressed to the point of migraine and wound up tighter than Piers Morgan during an interview with a papoose-wearing millennial. I used to love the feeling that an ice cold beer would give me, instantly numbing the stress of the day and enabling me to relax, the weight of the world lifted from my shoulders and replaced with a feeling of heavenly contentment. But it wouldn't last. The first beer helped, but the second and third would add nothing beneficial. Indeed, the cumulative effect would make me feel sleepy, bloated and eventually miserable. My nights would also be plagued by crazy beer dreams, the kind that inhabit that weird place between sleep and consciousness, playing on your paranoia and concocting fantastical situations that

26

actually increase your level of tiredness. You know the kind: you're back in your school classroom with your old friends, your current neighbour and newsreader Huw Edwards, you're daring each other to leap over the River Thames but in doing so realise none of you can swim and that you've accidentally set fire to your shoes.

Come the morning, you struggle to get out of bed, your head is pounding and you discover the remains of the half eaten kebab that you vaguely remember buying from the greasy van next to the A37. Add children into the mix and you have the perfect recipe for a day of suffering.

Running, on the other hand, is an incredible stress reliever, capable of achieving things that alcohol simply can't. The issues and situations that are causing you stress are numbed with alcohol, but with running you get the time and clarity you need to work through those issues and find a resolution that doesn't leave you with a hangover and a craving for bacon (although I freely admit to having followed more than the odd run with a fry up).

It must be something to do with the increased blood circulation and oxygen intake - my white coat-wearing friends can hopefully back me up here - but I have always found that running helps me to see things more clearly, to compartmentalise problems and focus on the issues that really matter.

Indeed, this perception is grounded in science, as a major study published in *The Lancet* in 2018* found that people who exercised had 43.2 percent fewer days of poor mental health each month than those who didn't exercise. The study of over a million adults in the US also found that those who exercised aerobically - through running or

27

cycling for example - had a 20.1 percent lower mental health burden than non-exercisers. Furthermore, the study found that those who exercised at least three times a week had an even lower mental health burden. So, cutting to the chase, regular runners have better mental health than those living sedentary lives. Fact. And running during the working day provides a prime, real-life example of *The Lancet*'s findings.

As mentioned earlier, I have made a habit of running during my lunch breaks for as long as I can recall. Once you get over the fact that you have to plan in advance, bring shower essentials with you and return to the office looking like you've had a sauna, it's incredibly liberating. It's also a fantastic way to shake off the stress of the morning.

Lengthy meetings, office politics, deadlines and mounting piles of work can all contribute to increased stress levels by the time the clock strikes 1pm. So, taking yourself away from the office and pounding the streets for half an hour may seem counterintuitive, but the reality is that it allows you to shake off this stress and the mounting tiredness that can creep up on you over the course of the morning. I'm no physio, but I also know my own body and sitting for hours at a desk leaves me with lower back and neck ache, as well as a tightness across my shoulders. I will have inevitably sunk into a hunch over the course of the morning, my spine like a banana and my overall posture like that of Notre Dame's most famous resident.

It's uncomfortable, saps my energy and makes me hate the fact that I work in an office.

Lunch runs - especially the ones where you push yourself and target segment PBs on Strava - are the perfect tonic. You make your way to the toilet, leave Clark Kent in a cubicle and emerge as the office Superman, complete with tights in the winter. The side glances from all those making their way to the canteen or queuing for the lift having bought their burritos, say: "look at this guy, I wish I was as athletically keen and ruggedly handsome as him." Or, as is more likely; "Twat!"

Regardless of the onlookers you head on out into the world, lock on to GPS and set off on a familiar route, a soundtrack of uplifting tunes propelling you on your way. As the kilometres go by you can feel the stress dissipating, the tightness in your shoulders fading and the joints in your spine realigning. It's like going to a spa, just without the dressing gowns, scented candles and plinky plonky music.

Half an hour later you return to work feeling paradoxically re-energised. Others may quietly resent having to share an office with a profusely sweating and rather smug-looking colleague, but, well, I couldn't give a shit. I've found that my own levels of creativity and productivity are increased on post-run afternoons. I get more done and I'm generally less of a grouch, so it's a win-win, for me and everyone who works with me.

It was coincidentally one late morning on a day in the office - prior to a lunch-time run - that my phone rang with an unrecognised number that would change my world forever.

29

*https://www.thelancet.com/journals/lanpsy/article/PII S2215-0366(18)30227-X/fulltext

Chapter 5 - The Health Check

Before we turn 40 those of us in the UK often look upon the National Health Service (NHS) as a resource that can help us recover from the minor illnesses, bumps and sprains that our youthful selves pick up in the course of living a relatively carefree life. We may well have visited the doctors for coughs and colds, had the occasional trip to A&E following a drunken night out or, more recently, seen the incredible work of the midwives and doctor up close and personal during the birth of our children. However, up to this point the NHS has never really taken much of a proactive interest in our lives. The relationship has been essentially one directional, us to them in times of need.

Upon turning 40 you don't expect that to change either. The year is just a number and your need for support from the NHS remains the same as it was at 39. Indeed, I doubt anyone turns 40 and immediately assumes that major parts of their body will either stop working as a result of four decades of use, or require third party support to continue doing what they had previously done for themselves. Yes, I had noticed that I had a few more aches and pains from running and weekly badminton, the sort my younger self would never have had to worry about, but I didn't think I was doing too badly. I was still managing to clock up 20 or so miles a week around the pavements of my home town and was making a vague attempt to look like a half decent badminton player with a group of similarly mediocre dads once a week on a Wednesday night. Mind you, very few of our badminton meetings have ever gone by without at least one of us being strapped up to the hilt and moaning about a dodgy knee, back, shoulder, hip or calf muscle. Tubigrip and Deep Heat have done very well out of our little group.

I was surprised, therefore, to receive a flyer through my front door a few weeks after turning 40, inviting me to a free health check to look for signs of heart disease, diabetes and other similarly alarming conditions. For the first time that year I was left pondering my health and the reasons behind the NHS's sudden interest in it. I thought health checks like this were for people in their 60s and 70s, what was this leaflet expecting to find, or keen to rule out, for those of us turning 40? Had 40 years worth of Haribo actually turned me diabetic? It was intriguing. I was intrigued. I had also recently had a conversation with my mum in which she had urged me to get my cholesterol checked, I suspect as a result of witnessing me demolish a cheeseboard the preceding Christmas. So, I called my local surgery and booked myself in.

This simple act, however, put me in the minority in respect of my peers as apparently 66 percent of 40-44 year-olds in the UK don't bother to attend their free health checks*, a figure that I was later to find utterly staggering given the significance my 20-minute health check would have on the rest of my life. Mind you, the national figure for attendance across all age groups, 40-74, is a paltry 41 percent, so ambivalence towards personal wellbeing is clearly an issue for all adults.

"Did you fill in the form?," asked the helpful receptionist when I checked into the surgery on the day of my health check appointment.

"No, sorry, what form?"

"Oh no problem, here's a copy, fill it in and give it back to me and then pop over there to do your own blood pressure."

"Do my own what now? Isn't that something that you have to be trained to do?"

"Nope. Just stick your arm in that machine, press the button and away you go."

So fascinated was I with the prospect of measuring my own blood pressure that I rattled my way through the form, ticked all the boxes, signed it and threw it back in the direction of the receptionist before heading over to the blood pressure machine for a play. Tucked away behind a *Carry On Nurse*-style screen, the machine was somewhat of an anti-climax and simply required me to sit down, stick my hand through an arm-shaped hole and press a button. A minute or so later a print out told me that my blood pressure was something over something and the fun was over.

All that was left now was a few minutes' wait before I was called through to the nurse's office, where a rolled up sleeve, some inane chatter about the weather, two tubes of freshly extracted blood, height and weight measurements later I was heading for the exit and en route to work. The entire experience was put out of mind within minutes of leaving the surgery and as I re-entered the world of Sherlock Holmes via the medium of the audiobook I had been listening to in the car during my commute to the office. Easy.

Two days later, however, my mobile rings while I'm sat at my desk. No Caller ID. I nonchalantly pick it up expecting to hear the standard spiel regarding the car crash I didn't have six months ago, or the PPI claim I've been foolishly forgetting for all these years.

"Mr Beynon?"

"Yes"

"I'm calling from the surgery regarding your blood test. The doctor is wondering whether he could arrange a routine appointment with you to discuss the fact that your PSA level is slightly raised?"

"Um, yes ok," I hear myself saying, as if this entirely new acronym is something I'm familiar with, and I arrange an appointment for the following week before politely thanking the news deliverer and hanging up. My appointment with the GP to discuss my health check results had been booked in for a further two weeks' time, so this 'routine appointment' was obviously not routine enough to wait until then. Of course, the only sensible option left open to a sensible person like me was to do the sensible thing and scare myself stupid by Googling 'PSA,' which is exactly what I did. What followed was utterly surreal. I was sat at my desk, with phones ringing and colleagues chattering around me, staring at my phone's screen and looking at the words 'a one in four chance of cancer.' I felt detached from reality, cold and sick. More rapid Googling followed, the fear intensifying with every result. 'A raised PSA could be an indication of prostate cancer,' said Google.

Prostate cancer.

I could have prostate cancer.

The one in four statistic immediately swam around my mind. I had no knowledge of prostate cancer whatsoever. I knew it was something to do with my downstairs equipment, and I vaguely remembered an episode of *Family Guy* when Peter was traumatised by the gloved finger of Dr Hartman, but my prostate was as otherwise alien to me. The internet did not help matters either. In those first few minutes I was overloaded with information from sources whose relevance and authority I had no awareness of. All I was seeing was an equal array of both pessimistic and optimistic interpretations of this particular statistic. *A raised PSA could mean a one in four chance of prostate cancer*, versus *75 percent of those with a raised PSA don't have cancer*. I had no idea whether my glass was half full or half empty, I just knew I needed a glass of something right now. This was too much to take in. The doctor's receptionist had delivered me essentially life-changing news with the same nonchalance as someone telling me that my flies were undone. Presumably she had hung up the phone and gone about her day, sipping her tea and chomping on a digestive, totally unaware that she had left me sat in a Basingstoke office feeling like the bottom had just fallen out of my world.

Making some kind of ridiculous excuse for taking an early lunch at 10am, I stepped outside to call my wife, however she was at work and uncontactable, meaning that I had no one to share this news with. I needed someone at that moment who could tell me that I was worrying over nothing - a skill my wife is well practiced at - but instead I found myself reaching for the gym kit under my desk and going for a run.

Having already extolled the virtues of the lunchtime run to you, dear reader, you're familiar with my love for a middle-of-the-day blast as a means to blow away the cobwebs and put the world to rights in my head. This run, however, was different. I found myself unaware of the fact that I was running at all, making my way along a familiar route on autopilot as my ill-prepared brain attempted to process the information I had just read. PSA, I had newly found out, stands for prostate specific antigen, a protein that is only released into the bloodstream by the prostate, the amount of which varies depending on a whole range of factors, from your age and family history to the last time you rode a bike. It is essentially a marker in regard to your prostate health, but one that can be affected by many things, one of which is prostate cancer.

As I clocked up the kilometres, my scrambled brain recalled the fragments of PSA-related information I had hurriedly read online, none of it made sense:

- The PSA test is one of the most hotly contested medical markers in men's health.
- No one seems to know what PSA level classifies someone as 'at risk.'
- No one can agree at what age men should get their PSA checked.
- Some say it's a good indicator of cancer risk, others say the opposite.
- Doctors in the US disagree with doctors in Europe on almost all things PSA-related.

You see how confusing this all is?

To make matters worse, sex affects PSA levels and can give an inaccurately high reading if you've ejaculated any time over the preceding week. This newly acquired knowledge therefore had my wife and I debating whether or not we had had sex the night before, two nights before or three nights before my health check.

"Hang on, the test was on a Tuesday, did we do it on Monday night? That's a Beavers night!"

"Yes, but Beavers is at 5.30. Didn't I go to bed early that night?

"I can't remember! I'm sure we did, didn't we? Or was that the previous Monday?"

So, in times of such high anxiety, at least it's reassuring to know that your bedroom skills are still as memorable to your nearest and dearest as they've ever been.

Back in Basingstoke, on the day of that phone call from the surgery, my early lunchtime run will live long in my memory. A moment in time, defined by an unfinished run on a familiar route. As I look back on it today, I recall stopping midway down a hill, a kilometre and a half from the office and walking back from there. I must have been in a bad place, because not finishing a regular route or a spontaneous run that I have mentally mapped out in advance, is one of my ultimate bugbears.

Under normal circumstances, I finish every run. Sometimes it might not be pretty, as I cross the imaginary finish line on the verge of being sick or beetroot red and sweating like I've stepped out of a bath, but finish it I inevitably will. Not doing so feels like I am letting myself down, cheating in a personal running exam or, simply, failing. Of course, I know that's nonsense. I'm not running against anyone, most of the time, and no one on the planet is going to judge me for skipping the last 1.5km of a run that they didn't know I was running in the first place. However, it still feels like cheating and I can't honestly recall another time in recent memory when I've bailed on a training run, injury aside.

But, on that day, as I walked down that hill, there was a 25 percent chance that I had cancer. My legs couldn't do it, I felt nauseous and my mind was spinning. I didn't want to be running any more. I wanted to be at home. So I walked back to the office, dodged the shower, picked up my bag and laptop and headed for the door, mumbling a random excuse for my early departure as I went.

I hadn't even saved my run to Strava, something had to be up.

*https://digital.nhs.uk/news-and-events/latest-news/nhs-health-checks

Chapter 6 - Attention men

Before I move on and get back to matters of a running nature, I want to dig a little deeper into the debate around PSA. Please therefore bear with me as the following applies as much to men who run as it does to those who don't. Indeed, if you are a man who runs and want to ensure that prostate cancer doesn't stop you from running any time soon, read on.

Firstly, for some unfathomable reason compulsory screening of PSA levels in men in the UK does not currently take place.

Let me just repeat that. There is currently no national screening programme for prostate cancer in the UK. This is despite the fact that one in eight men in the UK will develop prostate cancer at some stage in their lifetime. No screening programme for a disease that affects around 47,000 men in this country every year. The reason for this, as briefly touched upon in the last chapter, is that the PSA test is deemed to be too risky, in that it cannot definitively tell you whether you have cancer.

So, ladies and gents, it is at this point that I will don my jodhpurs, reach for my saddle and mount my high horse.

The early months of my journey through prostate cancer highlighted two fundamental flaws in society's ability to recognise and support those who develop this disease at a young age. The first of these, rather sadly, is arrogance. The arrogance of 40-year-old men to be precise or, even more specifically, the arrogance of 40-year-old men to assume that they are as fit and healthy as they were when they were 20, and that they therefore have neither the need nor the time to attend a free health check.

I was staggered to read that - although there is massive regional disparity - two thirds of us Brits, on average, don't bother to attend our free 40-year health check. However, I can understand why this is the case. We are still young in both mind and, relatively, in body; we lead busy, career and family-focused lives that suck away our free time and when we're not either working or cleaning up after children, we're attempting to have a social life or keep fit. The doctor just doesn't appear on our radar until we've snapped a ligament attempting to smash a shuttlecock or been struck down by the world's worst man flu. Taking 20 minutes out of your day to be told you're fit and healthy...why would you bother?

But this arrogance could be putting young men's lives at risk. I was told at my diagnosis (more on this later) that, had I left it five years to get my PSA checked, my cancer would probably have been incurable.

Five years.

Here in the UK we are offered health checks every five years from the age of 40. So, if I had nonchalantly missed mine at 40, on the assumption that I was fine, my 45-year-old test could have been far more devastating. Considering that I had absolutely no symptoms whatsoever, it's therefore no exaggeration to say that my 40-year health check saved my life. Yes, I know that I fall within a very small minority of men who receive such bad news but, even if your health check doesn't pick up prostate cancer - and I truly hope it doesn't - it could pick up a wealth of other potentially symptom-free health issues that, acted upon now, could save you from more serious complications as time goes by. And it's not like the health check is hard either. Your GP is not going to ask you to deadlift 200kg, sprint around the car park or commit to a vegan diet for the rest of your life. At worst you'll have to wee into a pot and let the nurse take a bit of blood.

I also find it hard to believe in this modern age that men still refuse to go to the doctor's out of some kind of vanity or pride, believing that they do not require medical attention until it is absolutely necessary. And by 'absolutely necessary,' I mean when they are down to their last pint of blood and knocking loudly on death's door. Even then they may be more inclined to take a couple of paracetamol than venture to see their GP. Surely we've gone beyond this? Are we really still ashamed to speak to the doctor about the things that worry us, for fear that they may ask us to drop our trousers? What do we think is going to happen? Do we expect the doctor to run fleeing from the building at the sight of our nether regions, or take a photo of the little chap when we're not looking and post it on Facebook? These are men and women who have intricately studied human anatomy for years, they've seen everything there is to see over the course of their careers and, to that end, you have more chance of impressing Gordon Ramsay with a chicken nugget than you have of shocking your doctor with the sight of your willy. As for machismo, what shows more guts, facing your demons and dealing with them head on, or pretending they don't exist and running away?

In short, if you're living in the UK, haven't had your health check yet and you're reading this; man up, stop reading, pick up the phone and book yourself in.

One point to remember when you make the call, however, is that you may have to ask for the PSA test specifically as, apparently, not all local NHS trusts include the test as part of their standard health check. Your doctor will be able to advise you on this, but he/she may say that you're not eligible as you're not deemed to be high risk. I wasn't ever high risk, so, insist, and if they still say no, why not consider getting it done privately? Access to private health services in this country is not for the exclusive use of the noble elite and needn't cost the earth either. Just remember that most of us pay hundreds of pounds every year to service our cars, but not a penny to ensure that we're functioning as we should be. So set any preconceived snobbery aside and pay to get the peace of mind you deserve, if you have to.

The second societal flaw to diagnosing prostate cancer in young men is the seeming reluctance of the medical profession to offer PSA tests to those under 50. Yes, I understand the arguments against the PSA test that state that raised levels could be down to any number of factors and that testing could therefore cause unnecessary anxiety and, even, over treatment. But surely it's the right of every man to know what his PSA level is and to be given the chance to decide for himself how he wants to proceed.

On my journey I encountered several specialist urologists and prostate cancer nurses who described the PSA test as one piece of the prostate cancer jigsaw, an analogy that certainly rang true for me. It cannot, alone, tell you that you have or don't have cancer - a low PSA figure does not mean that you do not have cancer (if you can wrap your head around that double negative), - but, whether high or low, it can be an indicator that something is amiss. The jigsaw is completed through the addition of its other pieces, namely further PSA tests, urine tests, a digital rectal exam (Dr Hartman-style), an MRI scan and/or targeted biopsies.

Prostate cancer is rare in young men, but I would hate to think that men who receive life-changing diagnoses in their 50s or 60s could have been spared such pain if they had been offered a test in their 40s that may have picked up their cancer at a much earlier, treatable stage. Of course, testing isn't cheap and I can also understand the reluctance of authorities to instigate a screening programme that is both costly and unreliable, but surely the fact that I knew absolutely nothing about PSA until the doctor's secretary called me, suggests that men in their 40s, like me, are utterly oblivious to their prostate health. This is a bitterly ironic situation as our semen-producing prostates have probably been at their most active over the preceding two decades and responsible for some of the best moments of our lives. We've essentially been driving a Ferrari for our adult years, assuming that every time we get behind the wheel it will give us the ride of our life. None of us have ever even considered what's under the hood making it go, let alone had a suitably gloved mechanic open up the bonnet to take a look for us.

Since our school years society has done a good job of telling us about the risks of smoking, drinking and sedentary lifestyles. We know, or at least we think we know, what it is that we should be keeping an eye on. We have, for example, all been checking our balls for lumps for years, thanks to some excellent messaging around testicular cancer that has hit home with under 40s over the past decade. We are aware of the risks of sunburn and skin cancer, we know that we need to exercise to fend off heart disease and we have a general awareness of other commonly discussed health concerns. But we know nothing about our prostates, what we should be doing to keep them healthy, what we should look out for and when we should seek medical advice. I'd say that, at age 40, most men would have more chance of locating the island of Nauru on a map of the world than they would of identifying their own prostates on a map of their bodies.

The 40-year health check therefore strikes me as the perfect opportunity for our doctors to begin our mid-life education and to, at the very least, make us aware of our prostates and why we - or rather they - need to be keeping an eye on them in the years that follow. I can guarantee that the vast majority of men who do attend their health check, go into it with no thought about anything other than their cholesterol, blood pressure and risk of heart disease, and of course that alone can be enough to cause many men anxiety. But this is the NHS's chance to give us a heads up to prostate cancer and to offer us the chance to discover our baseline PSA, a figure which will allow us to tell whether or not it has gone up or down in the years ahead. If a healthy man has a PSA test at 40 to show that his baseline figure is less than one nanogram per millilitre (ng/ml), an increase to 3.4ng/ml at age 50 will give the medical profession a way of assessing the acceleration of his PSA increase over the intervening 10 years. Had he not had the test at 40, there would be no way of telling what his baseline had been and therefore how 'abnormal' a figure of 3.4ng/ml is in his case.

So, I am in no doubt as to where I stand on the PSA debate. I believe it is a valid test for prostate cancer when taken as a standalone piece of the jigsaw. The argument that it can lead to anxiety and over treatment is understandable - most men with a high PSA don't have cancer after all - but as the other pieces of the jigsaw will help to paint a more accurate picture, I'd hope that invasive testing and over treatment can be avoided in most cases. With me, I was offered an MRI scan prior to my biopsies. The scan unfortunately highlighted a suspect area in the apex of my prostate, but that enabled my consultant to target my biopsies at that particular area. Again, the various tests, when combined, painted a clearer picture for the experts to analyse. If anything, this should be reassuring to men. No one is going to rush you into the operating theatre based purely on the results of your first PSA test. This is a slow growing cancer and it gives you time to complete your jigsaw before making any life changing decisions. My advice? Don't panic. Listen to the experts, follow the process, complete all the various tests and scans and then see what the lie of the land is.

As for me, my PSA at my 40-year health check was 2.79ng/ml. For someone my age, the figure most widely reported purports that it should be below 1.00ng/ml. However, despite my figure being some 200 percent greater than this, the doctor I spoke to upon hearing the news was at pains to stress that it was "only just slightly above the norm," that I needn't worry too much, but it was probably a good idea to get it examined.

So, it was at that point that the first of many appointments was made.

Chapter 7 - Hello Dr Hartman

I f your initial PSA test is flagged as being slightly above the norm, as mine was, it may well mark the start of a series of repeat PSA tests, at regular intervals. My first re-test came a fortnight after my flagged result of 2.72ng/ml. I was told to abstain from sex and from "knocking one out yourself" (the doctor's precise words) for three days prior to the test and psyched myself up for the phlebotomist's needle, like a boxer preparing to step into the ring. The blood was taken and an appointment made to see my doctor for the results.

"It's dropped a bit to 2.56," said the doc a couple of days later. "Although it's still raised. So I'd like to examine you if that's ok."

"Yes, sure," I said, before heading behind the curtain, in stark realisation that the Dr Hartman moment had arrived. "How do you want me?" I heard myself adding, as if the doctor was about to paint my portrait rather than inspect my prostate.

"Just lie on your side and tuck your knees up," he matter-of-factly stated, in an utterly nonplussed manner. This really was not a big deal for him and his calm

47

professionalism was wholly reassuring. Gloves were donned, and a matter of seconds later it was over. While not exactly something that you'd necessarily wish to repeat on a regular basis, this wasn't the terrifying, humiliating or invasive examination that many might picture it to be. I didn't return from behind the curtain to find my doctor retching into his bin or frantically cleaning his hands with a repulsed look on his face either. We both sat down and he simply said that he wasn't sure what he had felt and that he'd like to refer me to a urologist to get to the bottom of the situation, no pun intended.

He also made it clear that, although he would mark it as urgent, there still might be a wait of up to two weeks to see the consultant. As I had a small amount of medical cover through my work I therefore asked whether going private would make a difference to my wait. It would, and he referred me to a "top guy" at a nearby private hospital.

The week that followed was tough. You weigh up in your mind all the options, you listen to friends and family tell you that the PSA is relatively low and that the chances are slim, you try and take comfort from that, but at the back of your mind there's a niggling feeling that this isn't right.

A week or so later I found myself in the aforementioned private hospital, awaiting my appointment with the consultant and assessing my first impressions of elite health. I'm no expert on the NHS, but it was clear from the quality of the chairs alone that this wasn't it.

There were newspapers to read, there were flowers in a vase and there were markedly few people around. It felt a bit like being in an office, surrounded by people in nurses' uniforms. As for the patients, however, my fellow waitees all looked as nervous as I imagined I did. The fact that we were paying for the privilege made no difference to the fact that we all just wanted to know what the consultant thought. I don't think anyone even bothered to browse *The Telegraph*.

When finally called through, the smartly-suited consultant sat us down - Alex had joined me for moral support - and read through my notes. A little umming and ahhing followed and he asked me to pop up on to the bed for examination number two. Of course, I was well practiced at this by now and assumed the necessary position without needing to be asked.

"This might make you feel like you need a wee," said the consultant, before proceeding to be a little more thorough in his exploration and, indeed, making me feel like I'd just sunk four pints and was in urgent need of the nearest urinal. However, the sensation passed as soon as his highly paid finger was removed and I once again found myself doing up my trousers and heading back to my seat to be told of his findings.

"Well, it all feels fine to me," he said, astonishingly. "In fact, you have a very small prostate. But the PSA is still a little high and I'd like to see that come down a bit, so let's do a repeat blood test in six weeks' time and see where we are then. Don't worry though, I'm sure you haven't got a significant cancer and, even if you did, you'd be cured."

This was all a bit too much to take in. Within the space of a couple of sentences I had ridden the world's fastest emotional rollercoaster; Yes, joy...it feels fine. Great...it's small (that's clearly a good thing in the prostate world). Ah bugger...another blood test. Brilliant...he's sure I don't have a significant cancer. But shit... 'even if I did.'..he's not ruling it out. Then again...he says I'll be cured. Happy days, I think, or is it? I don't know, I have no idea.

We talked a little more about the pros and cons of PSA and what would come next if my levels didn't drop, but in an effort to reassure, the consultant was keen to add that prostate cancer was so very rare in someone my age, especially as I had absolutely no family history and wasn't black. He wasn't worried, but he wanted to make sure. And thank God he did.

So, a stretch of six weeks lay in front of me. It felt like an eternity, or at least it did for the first few days, but normal life inevitably intervenes and the routine of work, school, kids' parties, trips away and other such mundane everyday activities gloriously distracts and six weeks almost becomes long enough to forget. However, just as your subconscious begins to believe that life is back to normal, the repeat PSA test looms on the horizon once again. Going into this one, however, as my previous test had seen the numbers drop slightly, I was optimistic that the slide would continue. I had also continued to do my research and was now wondering whether this whole drama was more likely to be prostatitis, an infection of the prostate that causes a rise in PSA, rather than cancer. The stats, my age, lack of family history and the fact that 75 percent of men with a raised PSA don't have cancer, all played in favour of this being prostatitis.

My return to the hotel hospital after the six-week sentence did indeed show that the PSA had dropped, from 2.56 to 2.3. This was positive. It hadn't plummeted, but it was heading in the right direction. Nevertheless, the consultant still wasn't content and suggested that "before we consider anything more invasive like an MRI or biopsy, let's do another PSA test, in another six weeks." Alarm bells rang at this. What was he thinking? Clearly the figure isn't low enough, but surely the fact that it is dropping is a good thing. And what about prostatitis? "Yes, it could be that," he said, "as well as cancer!" There went the rocket-propelled rollercoaster once again, I was at risk of getting whiplash at the speed of my changing fortunes.

Having composed myself, I then asked whether there was anything I could do to help it along and we chatted through the possible benefits of changing my diet. Research has shown that eating certain foods can have a positive impact on prostate health and slow the growth of any cancer. Such foods include tomatoes, especially passata, pomegranate, oily fish and green tea. "Don't go too crazy with it though," were his final words on the matter. Little did he know, however, that I was already mentally planning an online shop to stock up on all the suggested wonder foods as I was damn well going to do absolutely everything I possibly could to bring that PSA level down.

The waiting game continued, but at least now I had a focus. I was going to become a tomato-eating, pomegranate-drinking obsessive for the next six weeks.

Chapter 8 - The prostate diet

I've never followed a diet, due mainly to the fact that I have always been one of the skinniest people you'll ever meet. My DNA and nuclear metabolism have dictated that I look like Stick Man with clothes on, and that hasn't changed for most of the past 40 years. At school I was essentially a bean pole with adolescent spots and a wispy moustache. Indeed, rather than wearing my clothes, I would support them in much the same way as a wardrobe hanger, giving the impression that everything was either too big or too small for me. So, my weight was never an issue, other than potentially causing my mum unnecessary anxiety at the prospect of being reported to social services for the malnourishment of her offspring.

The irony was, and still is, that I have a big appetite and like to eat. I have always enjoyed my food and, although sensible, have never worried too much about what I eat. Prior to this whole experience, I didn't eat poorly, but my wife and I had fallen into the trap of all eternally tired parents (or at least those who aren't putting their showoff meals on Instagram) and resorted to easy, oven-cooked evening meals and simple packed lunches during the working week. We weren't as bad as the 'help us with our crap diet' TV self-help programme families that we'd seen on the box, but we could have done better.

The PSA rollercoaster, however, had given me cause to reassess my diet and for the first time in my life, I was going to cut out sugar, cut down on processed foods and massively increase the amount of fresh fruit and veg - and mackerel - that I was eating. If there was a chance that this could be the key to reducing my PSA level, I was committed to giving it a go.

I should also point out at this stage, that I am a bonafide tea addict. In fact, in my eyes there is nothing finer in the whole world than a steaming hot cup of tea (made by adding the milk LAST and not in the way the crazy milk-first brigade insists upon). It is wholly comforting and is the one thing that can set you right if you are feeling in any way stressed or anxious. Tea is a drink for all seasons and all weathers, it is as welcoming as a best friend and as comforting as a 15-tog duvet on a winter's night. Or at least it used to be.

Discovering that green tea, with its wealth of antioxidants and reduced caffeine, is good for your prostate health made me make the ultimate sacrifice. I shut away the Yorkshire Tea and stocked up on a respected brand of this wholly new green tea. For me, the prospect of this change felt like a seriously big deal. I would never have contemplated modifying my tea habits for any other reason and had someone told me six months ago that such a fundamental lifestyle switch was going to be forced upon me, I would have spat out a shower of PG Tips in shock. However, it was happening and, although I fully anticipated the green tea to taste utterly inferior to standard black tea - presumably like a cup of grassy-flavoured water - I took the plunge and dived in.

Thankfully, after the cold turkey tea withdrawal had worn off, I slowly came round to this just-add-hot-water, milk-less cha. In fact, it only took a relatively short amount of time for my tastebuds to accept the change and I found myself cumulatively saving myself valuable minutes every day too. Not for me the faff of opening the fridge, reaching for the milk, carrying the milk to the cup, pouring said milk into said cup and returning it to the fridge. Oh no: bag in cup, add water, bosh, done. This was revolutionary. I was time rich.

So, it turns out that green tea is the methadone to Yorkshire Tea's heroine and if offered the choice, I would choose it over the nation's favourite any day. It's supremely refreshing, it stays hotter for longer, it's saving me a fortune on milk, and it's helping my running.

That's right, an added bonus of being a green tea addict is that I am now getting a healthy dose of antioxidants, vitamin C, vitamin E, lutein and, most significantly, polyphenols with every cup. For runners, polyphenols in particular help to strengthen bones by promoting mineralization, or bone growth. Furthermore, they are a natural anti-inflammatory, can help to reduce both cholesterol and high blood pressure, can increase endurance and help to burn fat. So why wouldn't every runner on the planet start their day with a cup of green tea? It'll save you time and help to turn you into Mo Farah.

◆◆◆

Unfortunately, however, the time I was saving on my tea production was lost on the added time it was now taking me to prepare our evening meals and packed lunches. Who would have thought that making salads was so time consuming? A cheese and pickle sandwich, packet of crisps and an apple was so much easier than my new lunch of mixed salad with mackerel sandwiches, three different pieces of fruit and an assortment of nuts and seeds. However, the effort was entirely worth it as my prostate lunches seemed to give me more energy for the afternoons ahead. Although not entirely surprising, it transpires that a midday injection of green things and olive oil leads to a physical and psychological performance boost that cheddar rolls and Frazzles can't match.

I was also now starting each morning with a smoothie, courtesy of middle England's new must-have kitchen accessory, the NutriBullet. However, the consultant had warned me of the risk of hidden sugars in smoothies, so mine attempted to balance the sweetness of the fruit with the bland goodness of green items such as spinach. This, it turns out, works fine, as long as you always include a banana. The mighty banana, you see, is the food equivalent of an Instagram filter. Without it, you've got a rather ordinary, unpleasant drink, but add a banana filter and it covers over the bits you wish weren't there, leaving you with a much more satisfying and shareable end product. Although, not even the mighty banana can do much about the consistency of any smoothie if you run out of spinach and are forced to plump for kale as a substitute. Avoid at all costs.

The other markedly new addition to my diet was that of mackerel, a variety of tinned fish that I had managed to walk past at the supermarket without ever previously noticing. Again, my preconceptions had me believing that this would essentially be like filling my sandwiches with cat food. However, mackerel is evidently a pretty versatile fish as it now comes tinned in a variety of flavours, from your standard tomato sauce to peri-peri or Jamaican, with everything in between, all for less than £1 a can. I had no idea that tinned fish could be this exciting! What else has been given the peri-peri makeover without my knowing about it? Or is cat food actually much tastier than I imagine it to be?

Of course, the real reason for the increase in my mackerel consumption was to boost my omega 3 intake, which reports suggest is also a good thing for prostate health. But this isn't news really, a healthy diet with plenty of fresh fruit and veg, omega 3s and fibre, together with protein from the right sources (not too much from cows, pigs or sheep), limited amounts of saturated fat and exercise is sensible for anyone wishing to fend off cancer of any kind. I was just upping the portion sizes of things that are meant to be specifically good for your prostate.

I therefore passed the following six weeks by concocting different ways to cook tomato-based meals, washed down with pomegranate juice and accompanied by salad, salad and more salad. I also upped my running and by mid-way through this PSA stretch I felt fantastic. The change in my diet genuinely made me feel like I had more energy and I was convinced that I was healthier than before. I had to be, I wasn't demolishing a share bag of crisps every night and chomping my way through kilos of chocolate.

This fundamental change to my fueling habits was also paying dividends with my running. I noticed quite early into the new diet that my endurance was improving and my tiredness levels were dropping. I could run for longer, saw improvements in my speed and, interestingly, a reduction in my average heartrate. Eating well, it transpires, makes you fitter. Who'd have believed it?

Well, actually, the scientists have believed it for a while. Indeed, when it comes to mackerel and omega 3s, the benefits of regular consumption to the average runner are incredible. As well as helping to ward off cancer, an occasional helping of oily fish can…

1. Speed your recovery: Thanks to their anti-inflammatory compounds.
2. Make you stronger: Thanks to their ability to help you synthesise protein.
3. Eliminate Delayed Onset Muscle Soreness (DOMS): Thanks to their ability to reduce your level of perceived pain.
4. Make you react quicker: Thanks to their brain powering properties, which can make you react quicker to the starting pistol.

So, while I would perhaps draw the line at carrying a can of mackerel with me on my long runs, I would recommend a regular fishy sandwich - or at least an omega 3 supplement - to any runner, together with a better understanding of the role diet can play in performance. For men though, why wouldn't you add a food that can support your prostate health and make you a better runner to your shopping list?

Full of fish and running faster, I was therefore feeling really positive as my fourth PSA test loomed on the horizon. I had tried my very best to do everything I could to naturally reduce my PSA level. I had also made sure to abstain from any shenanigans and didn't run for a full week before the test. I was convinced it would continue to go down and really hoped that my efforts would actually have accelerated that decline.

A few days later I returned to the private hospital and my consultant for the results.

My PSA level had gone up.

Chapter 9 - Waiting

Waiting for the PSA tests themselves, waiting for the MRI scan that came soon after the upward trending PSA result, waiting for a subsequent biopsy and then waiting for a diagnosis.

As Brits we're meant to be good at waiting. Queues are our thing. We have a long-established global reputation for waiting patiently in line, it's a trait that others admire in us. We're not the kind to kick up a fuss when it takes three hours to buy a stamp at the post office, or an entire morning to get through passport control. We're at our happiest when we're wasting our lives waiting for something, following the zig-zag line, staring straight ahead and silently reproaching the visiting non-Brit who is flapping his arms about, complaining at the time it is taking him to order his burrito.

There's just one slight problem...that's all bollocks, especially when you're waiting to find out if you have cancer.

The blood tests, biopsies and scans are all fine, they're the proactive steps that you need to take to get the answer to the question, and they're usually conducted by smiling, professional people in white coats whose well-practiced bedside manner puts you at complete ease. The hard part comes afterwards, when you're sent home to wait for the results.

It's a wait like none other as you don't want the results, but, well, you do. It's the cancer patient's paradox, like living for weeks on end in the pregnant '*And the winner is*' pause of every final of every reality TV show you've ever watched. Indeed, at one point during my six-month wait to be diagnosed, I half expected to answer a ring on the door to find Ant and Dec stood there with a gold envelope, animatedly shouting 'CANCER' before releasing confetti cannons and asking me how I was feeling.

Those long weeks and months were hard, but I coped by ignoring every piece of advice that one would expect to receive at such a time. I didn't want to talk about it, I didn't want to cry about it, in fact all I wanted to do was carry on as normal and shut it away. So that's exactly what I did. I kept busy at work, I enjoyed time at home with my wife and kids, and I ran.

Working for a charity that supports injured and traumatised firefighters, I have written thousands of words over the years extolling the benefits of exercise when recovering from psychological trauma. I understand the theory, I have spoken to the experts and I have seen it work for others, but to actually live it, breathe it and feel it for myself was enlightening.

Waiting to find out whether you have cancer and facing the uncertainty of what life thereafter might bring undoubtedly leads to high levels of stress and anxiety. I may have tried my best to shut that away and to carry on as normal, but it was all still there, manifesting itself in the occasional short-tempered outburst, headache, bout of tiredness, loss of concentration or mood swing. My wife, on reflection, must surely have felt empathy for Melania Trump during that time.

Utmost in my mind over this period was a widely reported statistic that jointly offered hope, as well as the prospect of devastating bad luck;

Men aged 40 only stand a one in 10,000 chance of developing Prostate Cancer.

On the one hand, during the period of testing, there was therefore a high chance that I didn't have cancer, but on the other hand there was still a chance that I had defied the odds to contract a cancer that only an unlucky handful of men my age ever have to worry about.

As time went on, and as the tests continued, my mind increasingly leant towards the latter of these two possibilities and to thoughts of how unfair this was. Why was this happening to me and not to someone else? What had I done to deserve this? Why was I being put through this at entirely the wrong time of life? Why do I have to be the one with the rogue prostate?

Although I tried to keep active and not to dwell on my pending fate, negative thoughts seeped into my head during unexpected moments; a quiet day at work, lying in bed at night, driving by myself, walking down the street. I started to fear these times of solitude as I didn't want to reflect on what had happened or speculate as to what might be. So, when my mind started to wander, I found myself battling it in an attempt to keep the negativity at bay, trying to think of anything else other than prostates and tests. But the result was that this internal conflict just made me increasingly tired, irritable and unpleasant to be around. I hated it.

Running, however, helped immeasurably. It gave me the opportunity to literally run off the stress of the day, to escape the trappings of my mind and focus on nothing more than the path in front of me, the pace on my watch and the music in my earphones. I wasn't waiting or wondering while I was running, I wasn't 'that man who might have cancer,' I was just that bloke who runs.

It also felt like the most positive thing I could do for my body at the time. I knew I had a good base level of fitness and running regularly was the best thing I could do to maintain and improve that. By running, I wanted my body to get stronger, to essentially tell any cancer inside me that it had chosen the wrong host and that I was going to do everything in my power to get rid of it. A 22-minute 5km threshold run, accompanied by a perfect fuck-you-cancer soundtrack of 90s indie classics, became my go to stressbuster whenever the waiting between tests became too much.

Indeed, it was during this strangest of times, in October 2017, that I reached a new running high, beating my 10K PB by clocking up a 48.25 time in my hometown 10K race. I had been pushing myself over a 10km distance for a number of weeks prior to race day, hoping that I would finally manage a sub 50-minute time, something that had proved elusive for years. It meant running at a pace below a five-minute kilometre and this subsequently became the focus of my training runs. I would constantly glance at my watch and aim to maintain a steady four-minute-something pace for the duration of each session, later analysing the split times against the route map to see where I slowed and where I sped up. It was a fantastic distraction and meant that I was able to focus on a goal, banishing all thoughts of cancer, work and other real-world distractions from my mind as I ran sub-five minute kilometres as much as I could.

Crossing that finish line on race day and stopping my watch to see '48.25' on its display filled me with a sense of utter fulfilment and joy and I remember sitting on the edge of a road with a post-race banana, grinning to myself from ear to ear. Of course, hundreds of people had crossed the line before me and my personal achievement meant nothing to anyone else there, but I had done what I set out to do, I had pushed my body harder than I had ever done before and it had paid off. I was surprised by the emotion of it and, as I walked back to my car, I felt fitter, faster and stronger than I could ever recall feeling before. The thought that I might have cancer seemed ludicrous in that moment. If I could do this, and if I can feel this good in my body, surely I can beat whatever is ahead and whatever the waiting will result in.

Thankfully, my wait ended in December 2017 - two days after Christmas.

Chapter 10 - Diagnosis

The portrayal of cancer diagnoses in the movies and on TV ensures that we all have preconceptions of what the delivery of bad health news might be like. Inevitably, according to *EastEnders* and *Coronation Street*, the doctor will look glum and will sit the anxious patient down before delivering the end-of-the-world news and waiting for the water works to kick in. The character on the receiving end, meanwhile, will usually look utterly shocked - as if this was the first time he/she had ever even contemplated the prospect of cancer - and the episode-closing scene will end with a wide-angle shot of the consultation room. The afflicted character - head in hands - will be sobbing, while the doctor looks on sympathetically and the duff-duff end credits roll. It's a tried and tested formula, but it's not a true reflection of reality, at least it wasn't for me.

For me, far from being a devastating blow, receiving my diagnosis actually felt like a relief. Don't get me wrong, I wasn't exactly pleased at the news, but after months of tests and results, scans and biopsies, the confirmation that I had prostate cancer actually gave me something concrete to move forward with. I was no longer floating adrift at sea, I had docked at a foreign port and could now begin my journey home.

The day of the diagnosis, however, was a strange one. I was incredibly nervous, but at the back of my mind I had a feeling that the news was not going to be good. The results from each stage of the process to date had all pointed towards a positive diagnosis, so I was fully expecting the consultant to tell me I had cancer. My nervousness was much more around the unknown prospect of how severe the cancer might be. Was it going to be contained in the prostate? Had it spread outside? Where was it going to rank on the Gleason scale? What were my treatment options going to be?

Emotionally I had also shut away both my optimism and my pessimism by this stage. I had no time for people telling me to be strong, to think positively or for those reassuring me that everything was going to be ok. Positive thoughts had done nothing for me so far and were certainly not going to change the state of my prostate now, whatever that may be. Being pessimistic was equally as pointless, there was simply no point in thinking that this was the end of the world and that life was over. Pessimism can be all consuming and is an easy trap to fall into, but I was determined not to let it consume me and opted instead to be a realist.

Realism, I quickly came to realise, was the only state of mind you can trust when you're in this situation. By being realistic you are not falling into the trap of false hope that is the pitfall of the optimist, nor are you resigning yourself to the worst fate possible alongside the pessimists of the world. You can only deal with the facts as you know them at any given time and you have to allow the process to play out, however long it takes and whichever direction it takes you.

My family and friends, however, were not all of the same belief. Many of them knew the stories of other men who had had prostate cancer and, in a wholly well-intentioned way, told me throughout the lengthy testing period that I had nothing to worry about because of their experiences. My PSA level was nowhere near as high as John from the camera club's after all, or Duncan the vet's. Doris's husband, meanwhile, had a PSA level that was off the chart, but it turned out that he'd just been to a mass orgy half an hour before he had his blood test, so we can ignore him.

In fact, you can ignore everyone who has ever had prostate cancer before - myself included - because every story is different and individually complex. A person's cancer is as unique as they are and the outcomes of their treatment can be vastly different. The next patient through my surgeon's door, with the same grade cancer, Gleason score and PSA level as me, will undoubtedly lead a different life to me, with different physiological and psychological traits. We may receive exactly the same treatment, but our outcomes could be completely different. One of us may find recovery easier than the other, one might have resulting lifestyle issues, the other might not. The variables are many, so looking to the internet for similar stories can be a misleading and upsetting waste of time. You may read a story of someone who has done brilliantly, but a misplaced click of the mouse could equally lead you to a story of someone who is suffering horribly. In the end, neither scenario will do you any favours or help you to make your own mind up in regard to your treatment options, so steer clear of forums and feel free to completely ignore everything in this book. My cancer is not your cancer.

This may seem strange, but my advice is not to get your hopes up at any stage during the testing times, nor to let your mood dip and for fear to creep in. Try not to think too much about the 'what ifs,' take each test as it comes, accept the outcome and then put it out of your mind until the next appointment. The process will get you there in the end, you just have to go with it. Of course, to others, as I found, this may seem like you're bottling up your emotions and this can cause them concern, but try to explain that what you're actually doing is being a realist. By not talking about it or debating the possible outcomes, and by simply following the process, you're saving yourself the emotional strain.

Being a realist, however, does not protect you from nerves and waiting for my appointment with the consultant on the day of my diagnosis was excruciating, both for myself and my wife. We sat next to each other in the busy waiting room like a pair of lunatics with OCD, I couldn't stop my right leg from jiggling up and down while Alex flicked through magazines like Johnny Five in *Short Circuit*. It seemed to take forever for the consultant to pop his head around the corner and call my name, but when he did we were up faster than Usain Bolt at the sound of a starting pistol. I remember shaking his hand and making ridiculous small talk as we walked the short distance to his office.

"Hello Mr Beynon, how are you?"

"Yes, good thanks, nice Christmas, weather full, car park good, bit nervous."

"Um, ok, come in and take a seat."

Stepping into that office and taking our seats, I knew there was bad news to come. Already present in the room was a nurse and I remember reading somewhere, or hearing from someone, that whenever there's bad news to be told, there's always a nurse present as well, usually armed with a box of tissues. Whether this is a specific role - presumably that of Registered Bad News Specialist Tissue Nurse - I have no idea, but her presence meant that I had a good idea of what was to come.

The consultant wasted no time at all with further small talk and thankfully cut straight to the chase.

"Unfortunately the biopsies have confirmed that you have a tumour on the right apex of your prostate," he said, directing my attention to a crudely drawn sketch of a circle with a scribble towards one edge. He went on to explain that during the biopsy operation 20 days earlier he had taken seven core samples from the target area and that six of these had contained Group 2, Gleason score 7 (3+4) prostate cancer. The rest of the prostate, however, was clear.

69

The Gleason grading system, in case you didn't already know, is the prostate equivalent of the Richter scale and the news it can bring is often as earth shattering. Named after Donald Gleason, a pathologist in the 1960s, the scale reflects his finding that cancer cells fall into five distinct patterns as they progress from normal cells to tumour cells. He therefore created a grading system for cells from one to five, with one considered low grade and five considered high grade mutation i.e. by this stage they have mutated to the extent that they barely resemble normal cells. The Gleason scoring system for biopsies today awards two scores to the samples taken, the first reflecting the grade of the most predominant cells, and the second reflecting the grade of the next most predominant cells. The two are then added together to give a final score. In my case, the bulk of the samples were graded as 3 and the next most predominant cells came in a step higher at 4, giving me a Gleason score of 7 (3+4). In general, scores from 7-10 are considered aggressive and it is these cancers that require treatment.

Having been given my Gleason score it was at this stage that the nurse's training kicked in and, as if from nowhere, a box of tissues was produced and expertly presented to us. Alex took a couple and wiped away a tear, before we both set about a fact gathering mission to find out what the consultant's thoughts were in regard to treatment options. There was no prolonged silence and I didn't collapse into a heap on the floor, I instantly accepted what I had been told and just wanted to know what the options now were.

Surgery or brachytherapy were the two open to me: the complete removal of my prostate through a radical prostatectomy, or the planting of radioactive seeds in my prostate to tackle the tumour. We sat and discussed both options and why the active surveillance - watch and wait - approach wasn't suitable for someone my age who, hopefully, has a long life ahead of him. Of course, we had done plenty of homework on all the treatment options before this meeting and I was already 99 percent certain that I wanted the surgery. Getting this thing out of me and therefore hopefully eliminating the risk of it growing or spreading, seemed like a no brainer. I wasn't keen on the idea of having a radioactive groin and was further reassured that surgery was the right option when the consultant explained that, in the unlikely situation that some of the cancer was left behind after surgery, this route would allow for follow on treatment in the form of radiotherapy as a second line of defence. As he said:

"Think of surgery as the wicket keeper in a game of cricket. If the ball slips through the keeper's gloves and the cancer isn't entirely got rid of, radiotherapy is the fielder who will stop the ball before it hits the boundary."

The most British of cancer treatment analogies possible.

We talked some more and, having looked into the surgery and read about its complexity, I was reassured to hear that I would almost certainly be operated on by one of the incredible £1.7m Da Vinci robots that are often used for intricate cancer surgery.

71

So, a little over two months later, a team of surgeons - at the controls of a machine that would look at home in a *Transformers* movie - would set about removing my prostate. My challenge, in the intervening weeks, was to ensure that I was as fit as I could be.

Chapter 11 - Fit for surgery

I had cancer. It had been confirmed. There was no more debate and I had set the wheels in motion for a course of treatment that would hopefully remove it, in its entirety, from my person. The certainty that had been so missing from the preceding 12 months was bizarrely reassuring. Like being lost at sea and being given a glimpse of land, I knew the direction I had to travel and had a total determination to get there. Stretching the analogy further, I had no idea what the land ahead would look like, or what the journey there was going to entail, but turning back would be like sailing a leaking ship into a hurricane. So, upon leaving the consultant's room on the day of my diagnosis, I donned my metaphorical Captain's hat, plotted a course for surgery-land, raised the running sails and launched the Good Ship Beynon on to the rocky seas of the Ocean of Fitness...which is just about as far as I can possibly take this particular sea-faring analogy.

My surgery was scheduled for mid-February, around two and a half months from the date of my diagnosis. On the one hand, this represented another 10-week wait, but on the other, far more positive and proactive hand, it was a

10-week opportunity to ensure that I was as fit as I could possibly be for surgery.

I knew from my research that recovery from a radical prostatectomy could take anywhere from six-weeks to three-months and that, even after the scars had healed, there could be long term lifestyle side effects. Not least, ladies and gents, to my continence, something that would apparently require the pelvic floor equivalent of an Olympic-sprinter's training programme to put right. The alternative, however, could involve the unwelcome addition to my sock drawer of a lifetime's worth of incontinence pants.

Cancer is undoubtedly cruel.

For many men fortunate enough to recover from prostate cancer the aftereffects of their treatment can be devastating. I had opted for a radical prostatectomy, but surgery to the nerve-filled nether regions is both precise and brutal in equal measure. The immense skill of the surgeons, operating multi-million-pound machines to cut away and extract whole organs, is incredible, requiring a level of precision and patience that any of us who have ever tried and failed at the game *Operation* can only dream of. However, the shock to the system of whole-organ removal is traumatic for the human body and for many men, prostate cancer surgery can lead to incontinence, impotence and the psychological burdens these issues bring with them. A cruel sacrifice for the gift of life.

The thought of this horrified me. At 40, how could I live the rest of my life terrified of wearing light-coloured trousers for fear of an accident, or enjoy a fulfilling sexual relationship with my wife if I was going to be unable to rise to the occasion in the bedroom? Although I was pleased to have an outcome and a date to focus my sights on in regard to surgery, these thoughts did weigh heavily on my mind. I found myself on many occasions, staring at other men of my age in the street, on the school run, on the football pitch and in the pub, jealous of their lackadaisical attitude towards their own penises. For them, it was business as usual. No need to worry about wetting themselves - at least not until around the sixth pint - and no concerns on the erection front either. How was this fair? Why was it happening to me?

These fear-driven thoughts impacted my life in waves, sending me crashing into low periods when I felt like I was carrying a physical burden, a dark and heavy coat that I couldn't take off. Whatever I did to try and lift my mood during these periods, nothing would work. I found myself snapping at my wife and children, unable to concentrate on whatever was in front of me and just wanting to be on my own. I was aware that this was not exactly a constructive use of my time, that this wasn't helping the situation at all, that I needed to snap out of it, to remember how lucky I was that this had been caught early, that I was young and that I had a good chance of a positive outcome...but I still couldn't take the coat off. Was this depression? I had no idea, but I had never felt anything like this before and I hated it. I hated how selfish it was and I hated myself for those moments when I should have been enjoying time with my family but was instead lying in bed wanting to be on my own. I hated my cancer and my body for bringing me to this point. Why couldn't it have been someone else? Why was this happening to me?

While there are no answers to these questions, cancer makes you realise just how much we take for granted in life. Our bodies, for instance, perfectly illustrate this point.

When was the last time you thought about how much goes on inside you to allow you to breathe, strand, walk, talk, think, speak, eat, digest, pee, poo, regulate your own body temperature, grow, laugh, cycle, run, dance or love? We are each unique, yet our bodies all perform this myriad of common functions, every second of every day, without us being consciously aware of any of them, allowing us to exist and to live our lives in the way that we do. It's not until one or more of these functions stops working that we even give them a thought.

Such moments in life, when our physical wellbeing is called into account, undoubtedly also test our mental wellbeing as we surrender control of our bodies and are forced to put our faith in others. Our mental wellbeing is so intrinsically linked to our physical wellbeing that we need to bear both in mind at all times.

While I hope of course that reading this book inspires you to take up running and to stick a ballot application in for the next London Marathon, I also hope that it inspires you to take a moment to stop and think about how fortunate you are, whatever your circumstances. Not that

I'm asking for your pity in any way, shape or form. I am one of the lucky ones after all. Rather, I'm asking you to consider what you take for granted each day and how life might be for those who don't have the physiological or psychological abilities or assets that you are blessed with. When you're taking a walk, dancing with your children, enjoying a meal, climbing a mountain or singing at the pub's next karaoke night, there are countless others for whom such mundane, everyday activities are painfully out of reach. For them, if all you can do is spare a thought, offer a smile, stop for a chat or give a small donation to charity, it goes a long way. For yourself, meanwhile, I would advise finding ways to exercise your mental health as much as your physical health, and thankfully running ticks both these boxes.

But back to my post-diagnosis fitness drive.

Over the course of the weeks that followed, I attempted to shrug off the dark moments as much as I could and to file away my urinary and erectile concerns in my brain's '*worry about them later if they happen*' folder in order to focus on my cardiovascular fitness and the mental release that comes with it.

Having broken my PB at my local 10km road race two months previously, I was fortunate to have a decent base level to work on, so I set about training for surgery in the same way as I would have done for any other race. I mentally set myself a target of running at least three or four times a week, short runs on Monday to Friday, a rest day on Saturday and a long run on a Sunday. It was a pattern I have more or less stuck to my entire running life and which my runners' OCD now compels me to abide by.

Runners' OCD, in case you weren't aware, is a very real thing. It is different for everyone, but I believe runners across the world all have it to one degree or another. The lucky pair of socks, the 'go to' trainers, the favourite T-shirt, the pre-run routine, these are some of the subtler ways in which runners' OCD can subconsciously inflict the unwitting runner. Many may be oblivious to it, but I am wholly aware of it and embrace it as part of my running life, however crazy it may seem to others.

A compulsory Sunday long run is of course part of it, but my sweaty OCD goes far further. I have my favourite routes - my go to 5K and 10K runs for instance - and I tend to always run them in the same direction. But on many of my routes I have little things that I have to do along the way; the drain cover that I have to run across on a local street, the goal post that I have to tap on the football pitch that I cross on my lunch run from the office and the iron bridge, halfway down a favourite canal path, that I have to stop at, touch and take a photograph from. I also find myself crossing roads at the same point, reaching for a gel at the same time (not a second before the one-hour mark) and mentally seeing runs in Strava segments.

Am I the only one who has the exact same photograph of their hand touching a bridge across every month and season of the year? Well, yes, probably. But if you're a runner and you're reading this, I bet there's something you do on your regular runs that you simply couldn't contemplate not doing.

So as the weeks ticked by, through a cold January, I found myself repeating the same routes, time and again, comparing times on Strava, analysing segments and pushing myself harder to beat the preceding week's totals and times. My nerves over the impending surgery were pushed to the periphery of my mind while I ran, allowing me to shrug off that dark coat of self-pity in favour of my trusty winter running gear. Like being on day release from prison, my hours on the pavements, tow paths and trails of my local area allowed me to feel normal, to lose myself in an upbeat soundtrack or audiobook, to breathe, sweat and literally run away from negative thoughts and worry. At times, it actually felt like I was in one of those montage movie scenes from the 80s, like Rocky climbing the stone steps in Philadelphia or the Karate Kid practicing the crane on the beach, all that was missing was *The Eye of The Tiger* in my earphones. I was taking on an invisible enemy, training as hard as I could to fight my nemesis, to win the day, to be Rocky.

It worked. I felt myself getting fitter and stronger and as the February date drew nearer, I knew that I was in good shape. I had trained well, I had eaten well, I had even slept well and, had I been about to enter another 10K, I felt like I had a good chance of setting another PB. The fact that I had cancer and was about to undergo major surgery made it a very different kind of race, but I was ready.

Chapter 12 - Under the knife

There are very few situations in life where you go into something knowing that you'll come out of it the other end feeling pretty awful, with the possible exception of supermarket shopping with children. Most of the time, our instinctive fight or flight response does what Mother Nature intended it to and ensures that we turn on our heels and flee at the sight of imminent danger. However, in some instances, Mother Nature turns her back and pretends not to notice what is about to go on. Prostate surgery is one such instance.

Walking into an elective surgery unit, knowing that you'll come out of it with less of you than when you went in, is a strange feeling. I did exactly that, and felt exactly that, one cold February morning in 2018.

Indeed, to say I was nervous is something of an understatement. I had slept badly the night before and although I was now keen to get it over and done with, I was also unspeakably anxious as to what life would be like afterwards. It all felt so unreal. My pre-surgery training had gone brilliantly and I felt fitter than I had in a long time, so I knew I was in good shape for my recovery. Nevertheless, voluntarily placing myself in a situation where, within a few hours, I would be without a part of me and barely able to walk, let alone run, was hard to get my head around.

I also knew that I would be coming home from the hospital with a suprapubic catheter, thankfully inserted into my bladder through my tummy rather than my todger. In short though, I was not going to be able to wee as normal and would have some kind of bag strapped to me that would need emptying and changing. What the hell was that going to be like? How debilitating was this operation going to be? How much was I going to have to rely on my wife to look after me? How quickly was I going to be able to ditch the piss sack and get back on my feet? When would I log my next run on Strava? All of these things were suddenly going to be out of my control and that was the thing that was causing me the most anxiety. I'm not a control freak by any stretch, but I hate feeling helpless and reliant on others and within a few hours I was going to be putting my body into someone else's hands for them to determine what my future was going to be like.

Nevertheless, despite all of this, the part of me that was keen to get this over with thankfully took control, ensured my bag was packed, got me in the car, drove me to the hospital, checked me in and passed me my open-at-the-arse gown. At the time I checked in, however, I had no idea how long a wait I was in for and I knew that, if Alex waited with me, we'd both end up making each other increasingly nervous, so she headed home and, alone in my tiny, curtained cubicle, I was left to put on my hospital stockings.

If you've never put on hospital stockings before, it's a little like trying to squeeze a marrow into a condom, twice. It's also possibly the most undignified thing you can do in hospital, especially if you've got changed into your gown before putting on your stockings. Here I was, wearing nothing more than a glorified bedsheet and trying not to show the world my nether regions as I wrestled myself into the tightest socks known to man. Had I been watching someone else in this situation, it would have been hilarious.

Exhausted after the stocking challenge, I sat back and waited to hear how long my wait would be. Thankfully, I didn't have to wait long. Within half an hour, my surgeon appeared between the curtains, thankfully looking refreshed, awake and alert, all that you want from the person who would soon be operating on you. Had he opened the curtains, holding an espresso, sporting a five o'clock shadow and complaining of the mother of all hangovers, I'd have been hailing a cab in my stockings and arse-gown quicker than you could say 'reschedule.'

His news was good. I was first on the list and after a brief conversation about the procedure and having placed my signature on a few forms, he bid me farewell, to be replaced soon after by the equally calm and professional anaesthetist who, despite his manner, threw me slightly by telling me that I'd be having a spinal anaesthetic, as well as various things in my arms. It was suddenly sounding a bit serious and all this talk of spinals made me cast my mind back to the day my son was born and the epidural that was given to my wife. I recalled conversations back then about the risk of epidurals and being worried for her, and now here I was having the same thing...although thankfully I wasn't also having to deal with the prospect of delivering another human being.

And then I was left on my own again. Sat by my bed, in a cold and otherwise almost empty ward, more or less naked, with my belongings squeezed into a hospital bag that was tagged with my name, waiting for someone to come and wheel me down to the theatre. This was perhaps the oddest time of the whole experience. There was almost too much to comprehend, but far from contemplating life, the universe and my pending fate, I reached for the puzzle compendium that I had brought with me and cracked on with a crossword.

A short while later a cheery nurse whipped aside my curtains, instructed me to jump up on to my bed and reeled off a list of things for me to confirm; name, any known allergies etc. She then took control and expertly carried out a three-point turn to maneuver me out of the room, while simultaneously rattling off some inane chatter to take my mind off what was ahead. I was steered along several corridors, through a few doors and prematurely into the recovery room where I was parked for a few minutes.

Thereafter, another nurse - this time in operating theatre scrubs - appeared, read my notes and uttered; "blimey, you're young for this operation," as if I had somehow missed the fact that I was 30 years below the average age for a radical prostatectomy. "Yes, I know," I replied, attempting to do so with the kind of nonchalance you express when talking about the weather with a complete stranger. Her statement was a touch insensitive, but it was also out of genuine surprise – after all, she must have prepped countless men for this particular operation, the vast majority of whom would have been of later years. So, I could forgive her, especially as here was a person for whom making nervous patients feel at ease was a part of her job, and she was brilliant at it. She jabbered away, intermingling the same set of questions - name, allergies etc. - with talk about my job, family and the pending snow. And before I knew it, we were off again, winding our way through corridors and double doors, past surgeons in masks and operating theatre doors.

"Do you want to see the robot?" my new bed driver asked, taking me completely off guard.

"Uh, no thanks," I heard myself replying, unable to comprehend why I was being given the chance to look at the thing that would soon be cutting me up and prodding around inside me. However, in hindsight I wish I had taken a moment to have a look at the multi-million pound Da Vinci robot. It is a truly incredible piece of precision medical engineering (Google it) and, had I not been the one for which it was currently being prepped, I think I would have bombarded my chauffeur with a hundred and one questions about it.

A few yards further on I spotted a sign for the anaesthetic room and sure enough I was asked to hop off my ward bed and onto another, far more clinical looking bed. Again, in hindsight, I'm not sure why I was driven in my ward bed to the anaesthetists. Up to that point in time, I had complete use of my legs and could quite easily have walked myself the 500 metres from the ward to the scary looking anaesthetic room in which I now found myself, saving my bed drivers the hassle of steering a cumbersome bed all that way, and presumably having to take it back again.

Once in the anaesthetic room I was quickly descended upon by multiple hands in search of suitable veins and points in my back. The same set of questions was asked again, presumably as one final check to make sure that I hadn't been lying about my name and allergy status all day, and after that things all became rather hazy.

Presumably, a short while later, I fell asleep and was wheeled into the room with the robot where it, and a team of highly-skilled miracle-workers spent the next four and a half hours separating me from my prostate. Like my stag-do eight years previously, I thankfully have no recollection of those hours. I was present in each of these situations and my fate in both was in the hands of others. Thankfully on this occasion, however, those hands belonged to someone who had spent his entire career mastering his art and not my mates who had spent their entire budget of Euros on one apparently unforgettable night in Bruges.

Waking in the recovery room later that day was not too dissimilar to the morning after that night in the small Belgian town either. I had no idea where I was, I couldn't sit up or move in bed, I was in pain and someone appeared next to me telling me to take sips of water if I could. Thankfully, however, my stag-do hangover didn't see me sporting an array of uncomfortable and unsightly tubes out of different holes across my abdomen. On this occasion though, I had a tube to my left that seemed to be taking blood out of me and a tube to my right that looked to be full of apple juice, but on reflection was obviously my newly fitted, urine-filled catheter.

It was surreal, frightening and it also felt incredibly lonely. The room itself was busy and bustling as nurses flitted around between beds, talked amongst themselves, laughed, joked and exchanged notes, but I was feeling alien in my own body. The drugs that were still inside me were making me feel tired and nauseous, I was terrified of the tubes, bandages and unknown things that lay beneath the blankets that I hadn't the strength to lift, or the desire to see underneath. No one stayed by my bedside either and in these situations a primal need for human contact and compassion kicks in. All I wanted at that moment was Alex to be there, holding my hand, telling me it was all going to be ok and helping me to sip from the inexplicably heavy water cup beside me. I felt desperately lonely and emotional.

Eventually, however, the drugs began to loosen their grip and my emotional and physical strength began to return. I was wheeled - tubes and all - from the recovery room a short while later to the Compton Ward, a urology-specialist ward occupied by others who had recently undergone the same or similar surgery. This was a ward where those of us recovering from a radical prostatectomy were expected to stay for one, or at most two nights, which at this point - as I was unable to sit up for myself or drink more than a sip of water - seemed unbelievable. In less than 48 hours I would be walking out of here and on my way home. Right now, that seemed about as likely as my jumping up and playing a spontaneous game of five-a-side with my new ward buddies.

Within minutes of my arrival, however, it was clear that I had piqued the interest of my prostate-less companions. Like a mob of meerkats - yes, I looked up the collective noun - heads turned in my direction and although chatting was not exactly on my immediate to-do list, they nodded in my direction and smiled. These were small gestures but ones that strangely gave me great comfort. Through a nod, a smile or a thumbs up, these strangers around me were showing that they understood, that they knew what I'd just been through, could sympathise with how I was feeling at that moment and were aware that I just needed to be left alone for a bit. I was grateful.

The rest of that first day was uncomfortable and painful. I felt completely helpless, lying on my back, unable to lift myself up and reliant on a handheld remote to raise the back of the bed up for me. I felt like I was trapped in my future 90-year-old self, dependant on technology to do the simplest of things that my failing body could no longer be bothered to do for itself. The rapidly filling piss bag that was always in view didn't help matters much either. I doubt I have ever looked more undignified, apart perhaps from the time when I reluctantly wore a pair of homemade Bermuda shorts to a friend's 10th birthday party.

The most unexpected feeling of the whole situation, however, was that of my bloated, gas-filled stomach. I felt like I had drunk four gallons of Coke and desperately needed to burp and fart but was unable to. The robotic, laparoscopic surgery that I had just been through had used carbon dioxide gas to expand the area in which the robot was operating, giving it more space to do its thing. The end result with this kind of surgery, however, is that the patient is sewn back up with a belly full of gas. I was told that this would eventually make its way out of me, but I had no idea how long that would take. Bizarrely, not only could I feel the gas in my belly, but when pressing the skin around my shoulders and upper chest I could feel bubbles underneath, making a subtle popping noise when I pushed against them. It made sense that the gas would rise, but bubble wrap skin and painful shoulders weren't what I expected from prostate surgery.

My wife and stepdad visited a short while later and, after taking one look at me, Alex - not known for her ability to lie convincingly - spent the next 15 minutes trying to stop herself from crying. My stepdad, meanwhile, tried his best with conversation but as I was not exactly at my most chatty, we just about got through the obligatory discussion around the drive to the hospital and the parking situation, before tiredness overcame me and both made their way home, Alex being comforted on her way out of the ward as if she'd just witnessed something horrific, which she probably had.

Nurses came and went, the curtains were pulled around me, bandages were checked, things were emptied and reconnected, and so the hours passed. When I was awake, I began to get to know the others on the ward too. Roger was in the bed directly opposite me, a lover of trains and a compulsive moaner he was regularly on the phone to his wife complaining about the length of time he had been waiting to speak to a consultant. Clive, two beds down, was a long termer and prolific farter. David, next to me on my left, had dementia and had no idea why he was in the hospital at all and Andrew, two beds to my left, was a young man of my age who had not only had a radical prostatectomy, but also extensive surgery for bowel cancer.

It was Andrew who first came over and introduced himself, immediately putting me at ease by telling me that it would get better, I wouldn't feel like this for long and that I would be up and about in no time. This, told with an infectious warmth, from someone whose treatment had been so much more severe than my own, lifted my spirits. Andrew was indeed up and about, walking gingerly around the ward, chatting and joking with the nurses and getting on with getting better. It was just the inspiration I needed.

"So, what's this bloated stomach thing all about?" I asked him.

"Once you start moving around mate, you'll be farting for England and it'll ease off," he reassured me. "Just don't get jealous of Clive, he lets rip all the time...showing off if you ask me!"

I laughed, it hurt!

David was also up and about and attempting to wander off. The poor chap would clamber out of his bed and head for the door and it was seemingly our job to call him back or to holler for a nurse. Each time he was taken aback at the news that he was in hospital and had to stay in bed.

"Why am I here? Where are my clothes?" he would ask one of the angelically patient nurses each time, before being reassured that he was where he needed to be and should climb back into bed. It was ever so sad, but also darkly comic. David was polite and thankful every time, surprised by his situation and obviously confused, but unmistakably British about it. The others on the ward were also understanding and repeated the same conversations with him throughout the day.

However, this continued into the night and, still in pain and unable to get comfortable in my bed, I remained awake throughout, kept conscious by the incessant beeps and sounds of the busy ward and by David mistakenly sitting on the end of my bed to remove his slippers and at one point climbing into Clive's bed alongside him.

"Ooh, I'm so sorry, I don't think this is my bed is it?" he'd say, not too unlike a scene from a *Carry On* film. It was farcical, but as I was restless, uncomfortable and awake, it was selfishly the last thing I needed.

Pascal, the night nurse, also kept doing his rounds, checking our temperature and blood pressure at points throughout the night, a practice that quickly became routine. Bizarrely, at the point of wrapping the blood pressure cuff around my arm, Pascal would also make a habit of asking me whether I'd had a bowel movement yet, despite knowing that I hadn't moved from the bed for the past 10 hours. It was part of his routine though and I respected him for it. Here was a man who worked through the night, every night, keeping sometimes sleeping prostate surgery patients company, checking their vitals, emptying their catheter bags, administering drugs if they were needed and preventing the Davids of this world from leaving the hospital at 3am for a stroll around Guildford. I could forgive him his questions and, as I lay there in the early hours watching him filling in some forms from behind a desk lit by a single lamp, I couldn't help but wonder how and why he would end up here, in this role? I would hopefully soon be leaving this place and returning to my normality, but this was his by choice and, if it wasn't for him and the thousands of others like him who take on the night shifts - and the day shifts for that matter - on wards across the country, where would we be?

I wondered how much Pascal was paid and whether he had a family to support - who I assumed would themselves be at home asleep right now. I thought about the times when I have got stressed in my job and how ridiculous that was when this man was emptying strangers' catheter bags every night. And I puzzled over the unfairness of life. How could Pascal be here doing this, earning what he earns, when Premier League footballers are taking home £100,000 a week for doing nothing more than kicking a ball around a field and getting massaged three-times a day? Or how is it fair for those with inherited wealth to be doing nothing at all, enjoying the very finest things in life and holidaying 10 times a year, when other human beings are working such hard but honourable jobs for next to nothing.

The fact is, it's not fair. However, when judgement day comes, it will be the Pascals of this world who will be the first through the pearly gates, while the rest of us will either have to justify our worth before being granted admission, or we'll be bypassing the top side altogether and making a beeline south. In this world, meanwhile, all we can do is vote in the right way to ensure that those who work in the public sector get the pay and rewards they deserve for the selfless work they do. Nurses, doctors, firefighters, policemen...what right do we have to criticise them, ever? And what right does the Government, for that matter, have to cap their salaries and extend their working hours? The only thing that is clear is that, despite the unfairness of it all, Pascal keeps coming back to work, doing what he does and helping those he is there to care for. I made a promise to myself at that moment, never to moan about my work ever again and to make sure that, at the time of the next General Election, I cast my vote for whichever political shambles is most likely to give the NHS the money and support it needs.

Needless to say, it was a long night and by the time morning came around and Pascal clocked off, I was desperate to get out of bed and to move around. I must have been in the same position for the best part of the past 24 hours and being unable to just hop out of bed and walk around was beyond frustrating. Of course, the fact that I had tubes sticking out of me and was still not really able to lift myself up without a helping hand, or the rise and recline controller, meant that as time ticked on I was also becoming increasingly anxious about getting out of bed. However, as the clock reached 9am and the ward once again began to buzz with life, my surgeon appeared in the doorway and made a beeline for me, smiling and with his shirt sleeves rolled up in the way that highly paid consultants often do. He was a welcome sight and, after pulling the curtains around my bed, he and a trio of nurses looked down on me.

"Morning, Mr Beynon, how are you?"

"Fine thanks," I heard myself inexplicably replying.

"Great, well I'm pleased to say that the surgery went very well yesterday. There were no issues, we were able to remove the prostate successfully and only had to remove a very small part of the nerves on one side. So, I would think that you should get a very good result."

I had no idea how I should respond. I felt like I should ask him a hundred different questions about the complexity of the operation, the look of the prostate once it had been removed, whether there were signs of cancer anywhere else, how long the operation took, how I should be feeling, what happens next? Instead, I said: "Thanks, that's great," in much the same way I would if the garage had just told me that my car had passed its MOT and was ready for collection. I was a little in awe of this chap, grateful to him beyond words and subsequently a little nervous in his company, but he seemed fine with my feeble responses and could probably tell that I was a little choked up. Mind you, that didn't stop him throwing me the ultimate curveball:

"When would you like to go home?"

"Um, wow, yes, home, ok, well then, I suppose today?" I once again heard myself saying, more out of expectation of what I should be saying than how I was actually feeling. I had heard and read so much from people saying that a one-night stay was the norm, although two wasn't unheard of, so I plumped for the former hoping that some kind of a miracle would see me out of this bed and on my way home. Internally, I felt like I could be here for a week, I had barely sat up for myself let alone stood up, walked, attempted to go to the toilet or tried to dress myself. I still had tubes sticking out of me and hadn't got a clue what I was meant to be doing with this catheter. Regardless, I exhibited an air of confidence to the surgeon that I was feeling well enough to be on my way home within the coming few hours.

"Great," he said. "The nurses will remove the drain (the bloody tube sticking out of my left-hand side) and give you everything you need to recover at home, and I'll see you in a few weeks." And that was it, a few further exchanges with the nurses followed after a quick inspection of my wounds and tubes, and he was rolling his sleeves back down and heading for the door, his work with me done. I, meanwhile, was left with a mix of feelings that I just couldn't comprehend at that moment. Of course, I was elated at the news that the surgery had gone well and that the surgeon had said that I should get an excellent result, but I couldn't really compute that information as I was feeling spectacularly tired and scared at the prospect of having to go home. How was I going to manage that? How were Alex and I going to cope without Pascal and the other nurses there to do everything for me. It seemed like a lot would have to change over the coming few hours if that was actually going to happen.

The first thing to change was the removal of the drain.

"This is going to feel really strange," said the nurse as she began to remove the dressings around the drain, "a bit like someone's pulling something out of the middle of you."

"Um, okay," I replied, feigning nonchalance at the prospect of feeling like I was in a *Saw* movie. "Just go for it." And she did, whipping out the offending tube like she was starting a petrol lawnmower. It was over in a matter of seconds and, far from feeling like my insides were being tortured - as I had imagined - it felt more like I was being internally tickled. Weird, but not painful. Mind you, I still had a sizable amount of anaesthetic and morphine in my bloodstream, so that probably helped.

Next, focus turned to my catheter, something that had, up to that point, been entirely taken care of for me. Pascal and the nursing crew had checked and emptied whenever was necessary, and I had politely thanked them each time, grateful but uncomfortable that they had to. Routinely handling and disposing of a complete stranger's urine shouldn't be on anyone's job description. We are all used to dealing with crap at work, but office politics and insensitive emails pail in comparison to the work being undertaken on wards across hospitals in every city in the world each day. So I was bizarrely grateful to be told that I'd be taking care of that department for myself from now on as my bedside catheter bag was replaced with one that could be attached to my leg.

With the curtains drawn around my bed and an array of tubes, bags and Velcro straps placed on my lap, the nurses took me carefully and patiently through the process for attaching, emptying and changing my leg bag. It was a lot to take in - with attachments, one-way valves and straps of different lengths - but it felt empowering and like I was one step closer to getting home. How I'd get myself to the toilet to empty the bloody thing, however, I had no idea. That was a problem for later, although at that point I had no idea how much later as I had no idea how long it would take to fill up.

As it transpires, catheter bags fill up a lot quicker than you think. The urine is effectively bypassing your bladder and being directed straight to your bag and, over the coming days, I was repeatedly surprised at how speedily the thing reached capacity. I wasn't drinking gallons more than usual, but my temporary calf-warming accessory required emptying far more frequently than I ever used to go to the toilet. Thankfully this is normal and it transpires that one's bladder is effectively a piss Tardis, capable of holding much more liquid than you would imagine. Water also seemingly passes through us with considerable speed, as the coming days and my frequent hobbling to the toilet proved. Indeed, had I had plans for a night out on the beers, I may well have required a backpack instead of the rather neat and thankfully discreet bag that I was gradually becoming accustomed to. Nights, however, were a different and slightly more complicated story.

The small nature of the leg bag made it impractical for anyone requiring more than two consecutive hours of sleep a night, so the hospital also provided a bigger night bag that came with a knee-high plastic bedside stand. This meant that at bedtime, the leg bag was detached and the night bag clamped on and hung up towards the foot of the bed. The tube connecting the two was around a metre and a half long, so the wearer has room to move around slightly. However, I spent every night worried that I would knock the thing over or pull the catheter out by rolling around in bed too much. Mind you, lying on either side was itself painful due to the fact that I had puncture holes across me that were steadily healing, but sore to the touch. The result was two weeks sleeping on my back like a corpse. For someone used to sleeping on his side, this was not conducive to a good night's sleep. I might as well have been standing up as I found myself lying awake for hours staring at the ceiling, wishing I could get up and head downstairs to watch telly, but effectively moored to my bed by a urine-filled anchor. Once I had nodded off, I then found myself waking up incredibly early, unable to get back to sleep.

Repeatedly having to humour two inquisitive children every morning who were fascinated to see how much the bag on the stand had filled up was also a bizarre way to start the day.

Once the nurses had completed their catheter tutorial, talk turned to attempting to stand up. Having nailed the drain, I was confident that this was going to go just as well. I was also desperate to try and relieve my bloated stomach and hoped that, by moving from horizontal to vertical, gravity would help to relieve the situation. So, a short while later the nurses returned to help me sit up. However, every tiny movement seemed to require a monumental effort. My legs felt like tree trunks, heavy and lifeless. But with help I eventually found myself sat on the edge of my bed and, having caught my breath, I was up and shuffling the daunting 50 centimetres to a waiting chair.

It felt like I was making progress, I was over the moon, but within a couple of minutes that feeling of elation turned to one of fear as I began to feel very strange indeed. My vision became narrowed, like I was staring down a blurry tunnel, I felt cold, but I was also aware that I was sweating profusely. My breathing became heavier and I felt a crushing pain in my chest. I knew that I was pretty close to passing out and I could feel nausea rising inside me. Panic took over.

I pressed the emergency button next to my chair and tried to get the attention of one of the others on the ward. I have no idea which of these actions brought the nurses back to my bedside, but I could tell by their frenzied activity that something wasn't right. The next few minutes are hazy in my memory, but I believe I was injected with something to stop me being sick, put back into bed, attached to a drip, given some liquid morphine and attached to a blood pressure monitor.

Sitting up, it transpires, had sent my blood pressure crashing to 60 over 40, a dangerously low reading that can, I found out later, lead to a stroke. Not what I was expecting, having been told I could go home within a few hours.

Back in bed, my blood pressure began to return to normal and after a short while I started to feel like myself again.

"Perhaps another night is a good idea," one of the nurses suggested as she checked my drip and once again pressed the appropriate buttons on the blood pressure monitor machine. It was an almighty relief. As much as I wanted to get home, I obviously preferred to do so with confidence that I wouldn't be passing out every time I sat up to reach for the TV remote.

This little setback had also drawn the attention of the doctors on shift and, having regained the ability to see, I was able to take stock of the fact that the men and women stood around my bed, prodding and poking me, were markedly younger than me. At 40 I didn't consider myself old, but this lot had to be in their 20s. They looked perky, lithe and fresh skinned, like they were straight out of an *X Factor* audition or about to embark on a gap year to Thailand. Instead, they were practicing urology, specialising in men's nether regions and seemingly loving it. They were unfeasibly knowledgeable and remarkably reassuring, not what you'd expect from people you would otherwise assume to be interested in nothing other than meaningless sex and Bacardi Breezers. Why these brilliant youngsters had chosen to specialise in penises and arses - usually old men's penises and arses - I would never understand, but thank God they had.

Junior doctors have had a rough ride of late, daring to strike in 2016 over excessive hours and imposed weekend working, clashing with Government in the process and putting pressure on NHS departments to cope in their absence. It was an ugly time, but the public largely sympathised with the junior doctors, and rightly so. These exceptional young people and their families have sacrificed a lot to study and train to master a profession that ultimately benefits the rest of us. Yes, they will end up being well paid, but why wouldn't you reward people who want to help others by saving lives and easing pain? Nobody, meanwhile, should be exploited for what they can do, or forced to work to the point of exhaustion. Junior doctors, like those stood around my bed looking like Dougie Howser MD, deserve our respect, and they certainly got mine.

So, my stay on the prostate ward was thankfully extended for a second night and over the hours that followed I felt my strength returning. By the end of the day I was able to sit up and very gingerly stand up without feeling faint. The Band of Brothers mentality on the ward was incentive enough to try, without being self-conscious or embarrassed. There was no shame here in walking around with your arse hanging out of your gown, or in displaying your incontinence pants like an alternative Calvin Klein model. Shouts of "well done mate," "that's it, keep going," poured forth each time one of us would attempt to walk the corridor, or "fancy a walk?" as you passed by someone's bed. We were strangers, united by a common enemy and determined to defeat it by going to battle with our catheters and drips at the ready.

I had never previously thought about what life on the ward was going to be like, but I certainly wasn't expecting it to be like this. Our preconceptions of cancer make us assume that those receiving treatment for it are homed in glum, depressing wards, where the muffled sobs of weeping visitors are the only sounds to be heard. The reality of a joyful, laughter-filled place of camaraderie and respect - for each other and for those working there - was a wonderful surprise.

Shared hardship brings people together, whatever the circumstances. We saw it during the coronavirus pandemic and I like to think that those recovering from prostate cancer surgery in Guildford, and anywhere else in the country, continue to experience the same today. It's one of the best parts of the human experience.

Come the morning of day three, however, I was ready to go home.

Chapter 13 - Home

After I'd spent an inordinate amount of time getting out of bed, disrobing and attempting to get into a pair of ultra-loose tracksuit trousers, Alex loaded herself up with my newly acquired home help collateral and we gingerly made our way to the exit of the ward, bidding a final farewell to my brothers in arms.

A short while earlier, the nurses had finished a lengthy walkthrough of the daily routine I would be adopting for the coming weeks, complete with a demonstration of the twice-daily self-administered injections to prevent blood clots. Thereafter, an array of catheter bags and straps, medicated needles, a 'sharps' box for their disposal, various drugs, laxatives to help the apparently inevitable post-operative constipation (joy) and a jumbo pack of Tena For Men, were piled on my bed ready for my departure. I was bizarrely reminded of Christmas morning when the children unwrap their presents on our bed, although if Father Christmas were to deliver this lot on Christmas Eve, I think our little cherubs would be scarred for life.

After thanking the nursing team and the doctors, Alex and I slowly shuffled our way out of the ward and along the seemingly 50-mile-long corridor to the taxi that was awaiting us at the entrance to the hospital. Neither of us knew it as we slowly and precisely steered me into the passenger seat, positioning the seat belt to avoid wounds and tubes, but Alex had inadvertently booked Lewis Hamilton as our driver for the half hour journey home.

Pulling out of the hospital, our Toyota Corolla/F1 car accelerated to stupid miles an hour and proceeded to target every bump and pothole over the 12-mile route, causing me to cling to the sides of my seat and tense like I was on a rollercoaster. Every bump caused a different jolt of pain and I began to feel nauseous with the stress of the situation. Why the hell hadn't the council tarmaced these roads for the past century? I could see that I was going to have to write a stern letter to someone at the Highways Agency before the year was out.

Of course, in reality, Hamilton probably wasn't going any faster than I would have driven home myself, but the small matter of the major surgery I had recently undergone was clouding my judgement at that moment. The driver, to be fair to him, didn't deserve the feelings of utter contempt I was harboring towards him as he launched into pothole after pothole, but I was too focused on not being sick to raise the issue and remained tight lipped for the excruciatingly long ride home.

After beating his personal record for the Guildford Stage of the Rally de Hampshire and handbrake turning into the small space outside our home, we paid the torturer for his services, disembarked and walked through the front door of our home.

Turning the key in the lock and pushing the door open, the sheer emotion of being home overcame me and, as I crossed the threshold, I unexpectedly burst into tears.

Grabbing Alex for a supportive cuddle, I blubbed uncontrollably for a few minutes. I was home. After the endless months of tests and waiting, the stress, uncertainty and fear, I had got through the surgery that I had dreaded for so long, I had endured the sleep deprivation and intensity - albeit it uplifting at times - of life on the ward and I had reached a new junction on the journey.

The worst was, in theory, behind me and although at that moment in time I felt staggeringly tired and weak, I was just so glad to be home.

There had been tears over the preceding months, but nothing like the uncontrollable outpouring of emotion that overcame me in that moment. I don't think I had been aware of how much I was perhaps bottling up the emotional baggage that comes with having cancer. For so long, I had just kept my head down and ploughed on, focusing on the family, my fitness, what I was eating or distracting myself with my daily routine in order to block negative thoughts from creeping into my consciousness. Of course, people had asked me how I was feeling on countless occasions over the preceding months, but I hadn't been honest with any of them, not even with my nearest and dearest. I had taken the easy option and either said I was fine or changed the subject and moved the conversation along to safer ground. This was my way of coping and, although I am sure any psychotherapists reading this will be giving themselves whiplash with the amount of headshaking they're currently doing, it worked for me.

However, there's only so much water a dam can hold back and, after such a long period of emotional denial, my dam burst in that hallway. Like a physical burden being lifted from my shoulders, a bloody good cry was exactly what I needed and, after wiping the tears away - and the snotty mess I'd made on the shoulder of my wife's favourite coat - I felt like something had been re-set, like I had undergone a system reboot and was now ready to crack on with the next challenge, getting well. After a much needed sleep anyway.

The days that followed were restful but challenging in their own way. I had to learn to live with a catheter, to self-administer injections, to remember the assorted drugs, to go to the toilet, to climb the stairs and to shower. Each was a unique challenge, with a unique set of worries, but as time passed each also became a little easier and, as my wounds began to heal, the discomfort began to ease. I could feel myself beginning to get stronger and before long even the catheter emptying became second nature, although I doubt the surreal spectacle of emptying a bag of my own urine down the toilet will ever leave me.

Between the checkpoints of my daily self-care routine, my time during those early days was spent largely in front of the TV, watching endless movies and winning the F1 World Championship for McLaren after rising to the top of the sport during a hard-fought PlayStation career that gave my thumbs a serious workout, if not the rest of me. Indeed, on the one hand, with the children deposited at their grandparents and my wife doing more or less everything for me, I was living every dad's unspoken dream. No responsibility, no work, nothing but time to myself. But on the other hand, this felt like prison. No excitement, no variety, no exercise. Needless to say, the novelty wore off very quickly.

Chapter 14 - First steps

Seven days after my surgery, I'd had enough of binge watching *The Walking Dead* and was ready to get outside, with Alex at my side, to attempt my first walk. It was a cold mid-February morning and, having been told that I needed to wrap up as if I was about to head off on a polar expedition, I exited the house like a human duvet and took my first steps outside the front door. The irony that I was myself walking with the same pace and gait as a member of the cast of the aforementioned zombie drama was not lost on me, but being in the bitingly fresh air felt incredible and, once again, unexpectedly emotional.

Force of habit had also seen me obtain a GPS lock before setting off so that the occasion could be recorded forever on Strava. It would later be named *Fuck You Cancer: Walk 1* and would mark the start of a renewed love for Strava as a tool to aid my recovery, as well as measure my fitness. Walk One totaled 0.56km in a time of 12 minutes and 43 seconds, hardly record-breaking pace, but it was a benchmark and represented a tangible way that I could measure my progress over the coming days and weeks. For the day, however, it was as much as I could manage and the feeling of complete exhaustion upon returning to my familiar spot on the sofa was overwhelming. Clearly my body had some way to go, but I was over the moon that I had banked my first half kilometre and, as I returned to Rick and co in their relentless battle against the living dead, I felt more human than zombie for the first time in a week.

I kept walking over the days that followed, increasing the distance and marking milestones as I went. Day two - *FYC: Walk 2* - for example, saw me clock 0.79km and reach Tesco, while *FYC: Walk 3* saw me smash the kilometre barrier (1.28km) and *FYC: Walk 9* saw me walk the children to school for the first time since my operation a month earlier. I was making progress and feeling stronger as each day passed.

Of course, the frustrating thing about recovering from surgery in February is that the weather has a habit of interfering, as it did in 2018. The snow in the middle of the month was alpine in nature, blanketing the world in white, courtesy of the Beast from the East, and sending my children into raptures at the thought of school closures and sledging. I, on the other hand, felt like the child who wasn't allowed to go out and play. I had to watch on from the front door as the children built snowmen, badly, annoyed their mother with incessant snowball fights and plodded up the road towards the nearest hill dragging their brand new sledge behind them.

The snow then became compacted after a couple of days and turned our untreated side road into a sloping ice rink, with sturdy footed souls seemingly requiring crampons and ice picks to make their way along its treacherous pavements, while cars gracefully made their way sideways down it. My walking progress was unsurprisingly halted until the warmer weather returned.

Thankfully it did return and before too long I was back on my feet and back on the pavements, extending the distance and discovering a joy for solo walking that my running had previously squeezed into a side note of my life. Indeed, prior to this time, my walking had been either family-based or purely functional. Of course, I love walking with Alex and the children, discovering new places, talking nonsense and enjoying time together, but family walks are basically just an extension of the indoor chaos, in an outdoor environment. The average family walk for our household usually involves several high volume rounds of; "don't do that," "be careful," or "mind the edge!" as well as repeated demands for sweets or drink, at least one young person urgently needing the toilet and the other inevitably becoming too tired to carry on at the furthest possible point from home. They are not the idyllic undertaking that Visit England television adverts would have you believe.

Functional walks, meanwhile, are all those where you simply have to get from A to B for the purposes of whatever awaits you at B. These are the ones where you leave A at the last possible second and mentally time your walk to arrive at B with zero minutes to spare, bag over the shoulder, power walk, dodging pedestrians, skipping over roads etc. These are the walks that most of us do on a daily basis and, as such, are the least memorable of all our walks. How many of us remember that wonderful walk from London Waterloo to the office of Boring and Co on the Embankment at 8.45am last Thursday? They're not the kind of walks we lock away in our happy place memory banks.

Anyway, prior to this prostate setback, running had been my 'me time' and I would never have previously sacrificed that for a walk; family, functional or otherwise. Why would I? A walk was never going to give me the same endorphin rush or raise my heartrate enough to mean I'd require a shower upon returning home. Running was far too important to me to waste the time on a mere walk.

How wrong I was.

Enforced solo walking during my recovery opened my eyes to this simple pleasure. I had nowhere to be and wasn't in any kind of a hurry, so my walks gave me an opportunity to see where my feet would take me. As such, I wandered around the streets close to my home and extended my radius as I got stronger, seeing every road in a new light as I went. I discovered houses and gardens, trees and side paths that I'd never previously noticed. I was able to appreciate the hard work my neighbours had put into their homes and gardens, I listened to the birds, I said 'good morning' or 'good afternoon' to people, I appreciated other folks' daily routines and found a peace

110

on my streets during weekdays that I had never previously experienced while running.

On occasion I would plug myself into an audiobook as I set off from home, giving my walks a different edge and allowing me to lose track of time and, on occasion, my immediate geography. Indeed, I once became so engrossed in a Lee Child thriller that I found myself at my children's school in the middle of the day, three hours early for pick up.

Crucially, walking also stopped me from wallowing in a mire of my own thoughts and concerns. I found that having too much time to think during those sofa-bound days was not a good thing. I would end up feeling sorry for myself one minute and then hating myself for feeling that way the next. People kept telling me how lucky I was that it had been caught early, but at that time I certainly didn't feel lucky. I felt uncomfortable, miserable and frustrated for large chunks of time, and then guilty at feeling that way the rest of the time.

The other factor that weighed heavy on my mind during those first few weeks following surgery was the inescapable fact that I was now infertile.

Unsurprisingly, the removal of one's semen-producing prostate makes the potential for future offspring technically impossible. Of course, I was aware of this outcome going into the surgery and made a deposit in the local branch of the sperm bank, just in case, but I had not anticipated how emasculated it would make me feel once it had happened. I couldn't ask for a more fantastic and loving family, and Alex and I have always been happy with being a family of four, but knowing that there would

111

not be any future additions to our little clan was a bitter pill to swallow.

I had never previously given my fertility much thought. Our two children had been conceived without any issues and - although I didn't subsequently walk around the neighbourhood with a smug look and a 'my balls work' t-shirt - I just unconsciously took for granted that I was a normal, fully functioning male in the reproduction department. However, once that was taken away, I suddenly became aware that I was no longer 'normal' and, unlike those who had chosen to have a vasectomy, this decision had been taken for me, leaving me infertile and with absolutely no chance of a reversal.

Yes, we could go down the IVF route if we really wanted to, but cancer had taken away the possibility of any more naturally conceived mini-Beynons. The finality messed with my head. How could I be upset at missing out on a future with children I didn't have, when I was so fortunate to be blessed with ones I did have?

I was playing psychological tennis with myself and, as per most of my past performances on real tennis courts, I wasn't doing very well. So the distraction of walking was just what I needed, allowing me to serve up the occasional ace to my unsuspecting mental tennis opponent.

The combination of walking with GPS tracking technology and Strava, meanwhile, allowed me to tangibly assess my progress, rewarding me with statistics and maps that plotted the increasing distance and time on my feet. I would return home after each walk, upload it to Strava and feel a warm sense of self-satisfaction as I reviewed the segments, the inclines and the day-to-day comparisons. The technology undoubtedly lifted my mood and helped to drive my physical and psychological recovery forward. It provided me with a point of focus and - in a world with so many uncertainties – it delivered a welcome set of immovable facts; distance, time, pace.

To this end, I will forever defend technology's honour against all the purists who scoff at anything more complicated than a journal (which I also keep by the way). Yes, of course you can walk and run without a GPS watch and no one actually *needs* wearable technology, but what's wrong with upgrading from the basics? We upgrade everything else in our lives - our clothes, our food, our mobile phones, TVs, cars - so why not embrace the incredible advances in technology and use it to improve your health?

Stop to think about it for a moment. For £150 you can now buy something that, 20 years ago, people would simply not have believed possible. A watch that not only tells the time, but can also track your health, your position on earth, how fast you're moving, how high above sea level you are and a million other calculations that your old Casio could only ever dream of. It's witchcraft on your wrist, and we're lucky to have it.

Having said that, however, I can appreciate the freedom that naked running (without technology) can bring. It might not be something I do very often, but when I do, I have always found it to be liberating. Like writing someone a letter rather than an email, it feels old school and refreshingly different. And, if the thought of not logging the miles is too much, you can always add it to Strava as a manual activity later.

Eight weeks after surgery, with the catheter long since removed, my wounds having healed, several 5km+ walks under my belt, my audiobook library exhausted, my wonder watch having once again proven its worth and with the green light from the prostatectomy nurse, I felt ready to reach for my trainers. It was time, at last, to retire the *Fuck You Cancer Walks* and to log my first *Fuck You Cancer Run*.

Chapter 15 - FYC:1

I hadn't gone two months without a run since my days of 20-something debauchery, so as I laced up my trainers one mild, early-April lunchtime, I felt unexpectedly nervous at the prospect of going for my first prostate-less run. "Take it easy," had been the words of advice from Helen, the caring, always-on-the-end-of-the-phone Prostatectomy Nurse who was my point of contact at the hospital, but I had no idea what taking it easy actually entailed. I wanted to run, as opposed to fast walk, but I didn't want to dislodge or rupture anything and set myself back weeks in the process. How would I know what an 'easy' kind of pace was? How would I know if I was over doing it? The only way to find out, of course, was to quit the questioning and get out there.

Deciding to stick local I mentally mapped a route around some nearby streets and settled on a target time of 25 minutes, as opposed to a set distance. GPS locked on, I set off gingerly, looking, I imagined, like someone who was either running in ultra-slow motion or who recently soiled himself and was anxiously making his way down the road at an overly brisk and awkward walk.

I have never been more aware of my own body than I was over that first half-kilometre. With every step I was trying to get a sense of how my nether regions were coping with their first bout of bouncing. I may well have run past familiar neighbours and good friends, and they may well have either waved, wished me well or shouted to catch my attention, but I wouldn't have noticed any of them if they had done, so focused was I on whether or not I was in pain, bleeding or leaking. Indeed, had the Queen been partaking of her first official visit to our cul-de-sac, or the Cirque de Soleil of their first street-based acrobatic display outside No.27, I would have shunned them all with equal obliviousness.

Thankfully none of the above applied - and as far as I am aware, I didn't blank anyone of importance - so as the run went on I relaxed into it. I began to notice the streets around me, the fresh air I was breathing, the rhythm of my legs and arms moving in a way that they hadn't moved in weeks. I was running again and I was loving it. In fact, I'm pretty sure I had a grin from ear to ear as the realisation hit me that I could run without doing myself an injury and that this might just be my return to normal. My pace was steady at around 6.29/km - my 'easy' - and my route weaved around the roads I had been walking for the past few weeks. Flat, steady, familiar. By the time I returned home I had covered 3.91km and knew I had had a workout, the sweaty t-shirt and feeling of contentment were testament to that.

Fuck You Cancer Run No.1 had been logged and, although I didn't know it then, I would be running the London Marathon exactly 163 runs later.

From that steady starting point, I very gradually increased the number of runs I did each week, sticking to a safe distance of around 5km for a good while and enjoying familiar routes from my front door and from the office during lunch breaks, once I'd returned to work. My statistic of choice, however, was not distance or time, but pace. I became fixated on improving my running pace over these short distances, determined to edge closer and closer to my pre-op average 5K pace of around 4.58/km. By *FYC:Run 8* I was at 5.32/km and by *FYC:Run 14* I had it down to around 5.14/km. It was giving me a focus and allowing me to go out for each run with a goal that I could monitor as I ran.

I have always enjoyed pushing myself on short runs and 5km is a perfect distance to ensure you cover enough ground, over enough time to arrive home as close to the point of exhaustion as possible. Indeed, I find it very hard to go slowly over 5km, even if I set off to do so. This isn't my being egotistical in any way, rather it's more a need to feel like I've made the best use out of the time I've allowed for that particular day's run. So, a slow 5km feels, in a way, like a bit of a waste. I don't want to get home feeling like I could go round the block again, I want to get home feeling like I've had a workout and earned myself a sugar-filled treat.

Now, anyone who knows anything about running, will tell you at this point that I am a complete idiot, and they are probably right. Slow running is actually incredibly beneficial for distance runners, just ask Eliud Kipchoge - the marathon world record holder and the first man to run the 26.2 miles in under two hours - who regularly commences his recovery runs at a leisurely 5.45/km.

Kipchoge is not alone either, in 2019 Strava studied the training patterns of its 44 million worldwide users and found that training slower and training less can actually improve your marathon time. To be precise, it discovered that those marathoners who trained at marathon pace for 43 percent of their training runs then came home in better times - under four hours - in subsequent marathons when they cut their number of marathon-pace training runs to 25 percent. Which, if your head isn't too scrambled by that last sentence, simply means that slowing your pace can improve your endurance.

Slow running has also been shown to improve strength; aid recovery; reduce the risk of injury; allow your body to use its fat reserves more efficiently; improve your muscular and respiratory systems; strengthen tendons, ligaments, joints and bones; help you improve technique and form and allow you to be more social in your running. Like broccoli, it's entirely good for you. But also, like broccoli, everything else on your plate is far more appealing and, for me, I'd take a high risk 5K doughnut over a flavourless slow run floret any day.

At least this was the approach I took at the time. I was so determined to get back to my pre-operation fitness that I fixated on pace as the measure by which I could get there and - whether sensible or not - it worked as a motivation tool, at least doing my mental health good if not my tendons, ligaments and assorted other lower limb bits.

Seeing my pace pick up consistently as the weeks passed, also helped me to trust my body again. I had always felt like John Hurt in *Alien* while I was living with cancer, like there was something foreign inside me, controlling my destiny and entirely outside of my control. It was as if my body had betrayed me, gone behind my back and had a dirty, sordid affair before infecting me with the consequences. Trusting it, after cancer, wasn't easy. I didn't want to let my guard down and give it a chance to run off with the epidemiological equivalent of a drunken one-night stand again, so I beasted it as much as I could to bring it back in line and back to its pre-affair self.

Of course, as I reflect on that time and in light of all that I have learned about running since, I know that focusing on one element of performance can be counterintuitive. Running requires far more than simply putting one foot in front of the other too, there's technique, core strength, flexibility and proper nutrition for starters, then there's speed training, hill training, tempo runs, threshold runs and, of course, easy runs. There is a science behind the humble art of running and the more you study it, the more it draws you in. For now though, I was content with focusing my attention on pace and, on *FYC: Run 34* - six months after surgery, on an uncomfortably muggy early-August evening - I finally broke the five-minute per km pace barrier, clocking a 4.59/km average pace on a regular 5km loop.

Like breaking through a psychological barrier, it was a moment that marked a subtle but significant change in my thinking. Up to that point I had been recovering from surgery and from cancer but now, having reached the baseline I had established prior to going under the knife, I could focus on getting stronger, faster and fitter. This was great, it was like being unshackled from an invisible burden. I was raring to go. The problem was, I had nowhere to go. I needed a new challenge.

Chapter 16 - The sofa marathon

Sunday, 22 April 2018 was almost like any other Sunday. A lazy start, a prolonged breakfast with multiple rounds of toast, gallons of tea and a spot of Sunday morning telly. However, there was only one thing on the telly this morning and it started with a piece of music by Ron Goodwin, composed for a 1966 film called *The Trap*. No one has ever heard of either the composer or the film, but when this particular piece of music plays at the start of the BBC's coverage, it is recognised for one thing and one thing only, the London Marathon. Like Fleetwood Mac's *The Chain* and Formula One, Goodwin's distinct big band tune has become synonymous with the Marathon, evoking memories for those who have run it, inspiring those who have yet to run it and adding butterflies to the stomachs of those about to run it.

So, as I tuned in on that bright, sunny and soon-to-be record-breakingly hot April morning, I was greeted by the sight of thousands of runners lining up at the start lines in Blackheath, Greenwich and Gabby Logan - the BBC's ever enthusiastic sports all-rounder, who's as adept at covering the marathon as she is the Olympics, football, darts and bog snorkeling - speaking to the race's oldest and youngest participants. John Starbrook, 87, a grandfather of four - and the former of the two participants, in case you were in any doubt - was talking about the race ahead with as much energy as the spritely just-turned-18-today-year-old next to him. Elsewhere, assorted other BBC reporters, some more usually found on children's TV, were talking to various runners in fancy dress, playing it safe with the all too predictable interview questions; "how are you feeling?" "How has the training gone?" "What time are you aiming for?" and "Who are you raising money for?" Had they chosen to throw in a; "Have you managed to do a shit yet this morning?" I doubt they would be returning for the 2019 event, although it's a question every runner who's ever run a marathon would be fascinated to know the answer to.

The coverage bounced between the build up to the start of the elite races and the nerve-filled, lacklustre warm-ups being undertaken by the masses. At one point I almost choked on my bagel as Radzi Chinyanganya - a presenter my children animatedly told me was on *Blue Peter* - stuck his microphone in front of a group of firefighters. The group were running in full firefighting kit to raise money for families affected by the Grenfell Tower fire in 2017, as well as for the charity I work for, The Fire Fighters Charity. It was fantastic to see them and I was reminded that, of course, not only was this an event that I was watching out of a personal interest, but I had a professional interest in it also. The charity had a team of runners taking part in the event, all of which I had written about in our magazine, helping to promote their fundraising pages and recognising their training and hard work over the preceding months. These were individuals - some firefighters, some members of the public - who each had a genuine reason for running in aid of the charity, whether running on behalf of an injured colleague, in memory of someone who had been supported by the charity or as a thank you for the support they'd received. Their individual stories were compelling and none had had any issues with raising the £2,000 we had asked them to find. Imagining them all nervously waiting for the start of the race in the South London sunshine - as I sat on the sofa in my dressing gown, chomping down on my second round of toast, gave me a great sense of pride, as well as a touch of envy. It also got me thinking.

I had a story. If ever there was a time when a charity was going to consider me worthy of a place on their marathon team, this was it, surely. Was this the silver lining to the dark cloud of cancer that I didn't even realise I had been looking for? Maybe.

For the rest of the morning, I sat glued to the screen. The race itself began with the bizarre spectacle of Her Majesty Queen Elizabeth II starting it all from 30 miles away in Windsor Castle. For some reason, the organisers wanted us to believe that the Monarch was about to press a giant red button on a plinth that was somehow connected - presumably via specially commissioned Royal satellites - to a man on the start line holding an air horn. Her Majesty seemed somewhat perplexed, speaking at length to a button official, presumably remarking to him; "Seriously? Why are we doing this? Why don't I just say 'go'? Whose idea was this?" before pressing the sham button and looking a little embarrassed by the whole thing.

Once underway, however, the race followed a familiar pattern; I spent considerable chunks of time remarking at how fast the elite men and women were running, speculating as to why the pace setters aren't elite runners themselves and then pondering how the runners in rhino costumes managed to train. The commentators largely followed suit and, although the heat of the day added an extra talking point, the hours of coverage were filled with the joyful sight of runners winding their way through the streets of London, over and around the landmarks that make the race so familiar to millions; the Cutty Sark, Tower Bridge, Canary Wharf, the Victoria Embankment and The Mall. It was joyous, uplifting and inspiring, I loved every minute and, by the end, was in no doubt whatsoever as to what I was going to be doing that afternoon.

Indeed, like countless other inspired runners, I found myself sat in front of my computer later that day completing an entry form for Prostate Cancer UK's 2019 Virgin Money London Marathon team. I was in no doubt at all that this was something I wanted to do, but I also found myself with oddly conflicting feelings at the prospect of using my prostate cancer story to secure a place on the Blackheath start line in 12 months' time. Working for a charity, I knew that it was the compelling, heartfelt 'against the odds' stories that secured the hotly-contested places. So, having prostate cancer at such a young age was definitely going to play in my favour and I couldn't help but feel that, if my story wasn't going to secure me a spot this year, nothing was. Being excited at the prospect that the worst news of my life could help me bypass the ballot and achieve a long-standing dream, however, messed with my head. Clouds and silver linings came to mind, but it also felt like I was doing something wrong and perhaps denying a place to someone more deserving. If this was *The X Factor* I'd be on stage now, telling Simon Cowell the sob story of my life, with sympathetic music tinkling away in the background, hoping that he'd be impressed enough to send me through to judge's houses - or at the very least Louis Walsh's caravan. The cringe worthiness of the cliché I was playing out in my dining room didn't sit well with my conscience.

Nevertheless, I completed the application and clicked submit.

Chapter 17 - I'm in

My mobile rang with an undisclosed number and my heart skipped a beat. It was mid-September and I was at work, where we were coincidentally in the middle of notifying our own successful marathon runners of their confirmed places. I had a feeling that this might be the call that I had been anxiously waiting for, and it was. On the other end of the phone was a friendly voice from the Prostate Cancer UK Events team who cheerfully told me that I had secured a place on the Charity's team for the 2019 Virgin Money London Marathon. Further details and a fundraising pack would be winging its way to me, the expectation being that I would raise £2,000 for the charity ahead of race day. I was over the moon, quietly confident that the fundraising was going to be possible and grinning like I'd won the Lottery when I returned to my desk. I was in.

Sitting next to Kevin, an experienced marathon runner, ultra-regular and all-round running machine, meant that I ignored all work for the best part of the next hour, missed several meetings and let my answerphone take the strain as I grilled my vastly more experienced colleague on all things marathon. The road ahead was not going to be easy, stepping up to marathon distance was going to take hard work and, as we both agreed, should probably involve a visit to the running shop in the not too distant future to invest in an extortionate pair of new running boots.

By the end of the day, I had shared the news with colleagues, friends, family and any passing strangers who cared to listen. Most responded by humouring my excitement and congratulating me on the news, while I suspect secretly wondering why I would put myself through the stress and strain of training for 26.2 miles. Some, I knew, worried that pushing myself so hard, after all that had happened, was perhaps not the best idea. Nevertheless, they were 100 percent behind me and promised to help with the fundraising.

My own excitement, coupled with that of others on my behalf, made the day of that phone call memorable. However, as I reflect on it today, my abiding memory is not of the happiness, but of feeling an immeasurable weight lifting from my shoulders, as if I had somehow been freed from some invisible psychological shackles. I can only put this down to being gifted a means by which I could draw a line under a dark chapter in my life and move on with a new drive and purpose.

I remember feeling like I was riding high, that I had a focus for the coming months and, more fundamentally, that all the physical and emotional pain of the preceding year had finally brought me to a positive point. I had struggled so much with the 'why?' (Why me? Why was I the one in 10,000 to get prostate cancer at 40? Why was I having to go through this?). But now, that mental torture had resulted in an opportunity to prove something to myself, to fulfil a longstanding ambition and do something I'd never done before. If I could recover from cancer, rediscover my fitness, push myself harder and further than I had ever done before and cross that finish line on The Mall in April, I would have proved to myself that cancer was not going to beat me. And, like flushing a particularly nasty turd down the loo, I could then forget about the whole nasty experience and get on with the rest of my life.

In fact, I decided there and then that the London Marathon was going to be the last time I would record a *Fuck You Cancer* run on Strava. All runs thereafter would just be, well, runs, minus any form of profanity or disease.

Of course, the danger when you place such psychological significance on a particular event is that, should something like injury or illness prevent you from reaching your end goal, the negative mental impact could be just as significant. However, at that moment in time, I was fit, I was happy and my glass was very much half full. Failure was most certainly not a consideration.

I was also excited at the prospect of joining the one percent of the world's population who have run a marathon in their lifetime, although I knew that the months ahead were going to be hard if that prospect was to become a reality. In all likelihood, I would be running through some of the coldest and most miserable days of the year; I was going to discover - through trial, error and upset stomachs - what running nutrition was all about; I was going to be spending more time away from my wife and kids at weekends and I was opening myself up to the prospect of potential injury. So, yes, who wouldn't be excited by all that lay ahead?

All this pain and suffering, however, would require planning, so my first mission - once I'd calmed down and finished boring anyone who'd listen - was to search for a suitable training plan.

Chapter 18 - The plan

Living half an hour away from the office, my drive home is often achieved on autopilot, so familiar am I with every junction, turn and traffic light. However, as I arrived home on the day I had received the call confirming my place in the 2019 London Marathon, I realised that I had spent the entire journey thinking about the training and fundraising, formulating plans for both in my mind and paying no attention whatsoever to the act of driving. Of course, I had driven home safely and hadn't managed to wrap my Vauxhall Zafira around a tree, but the cast of the *Wacky Races* could have driven past on the other side of the road and I doubt that I would have noticed. It surprised me how little of the journey I remembered, so preoccupied was I by all things marathon, but I gave it no more than a passing thought before I entered the house.

Pausing briefly to referee a wife versus children argument over chicken nuggets at the dinner table, I quickly searched out a notebook and iPad. I was fully expecting to be overwhelmed by a Google search for marathon training plans and I wasn't disappointed. As you would expect, there are a seemingly infinite number of options in regard to training plans for runners of different abilities. However, regardless of whether you are running to achieve a specific time, or just running to finish, the vast majority of plans are based on a 16-week timeframe, the idea being that four months is ample time to take a novice to the finish line of a marathon or - as I hoped - to allow a half marathoner to double his distance in under four hours. Nevertheless, choosing a suitable plan proved to be unexpectedly stressful.

For a start, I have never been any good in restaurants. I enjoy eating out, but I find that the whole thing would be a far more enjoyable experience if menus weren't involved. When choosing what to eat, especially from a large and complex menu, I have a habit of picking food that looks delicious when written down, but is inevitably spectacularly underwhelming when it arrives in front of me. The pitiful looks of my fellow diners usually tells me that they are equally aware of my poor choice, but we carry on with the charade regardless and tell each other how lovely our meals are.

This is why IKEA is the world's greatest restaurant, especially for parents with young children. The menu has no more than three items - two of which are meatballs - there's no table service, it's so noisy you can't hear your own family and the whole meal is over in about half an hour. Heaven.

If only IKEA did marathons. Presented with thousands of options, I needed the plan equivalent of a dozen meatballs; something that was simple, easy to digest and unlikely to disappoint. I also wanted a plan that would allow a degree of flexibility and that didn't involve too much strength training or cross training. Finding the time to run was going to be hard enough around work and family life, so I knew that adding regular weights, swimming and yoga to the weekly schedule would probably have seen me running my way to the divorce courts. Yes, of course I am aware that omitting these vital components was not going to improve my chances of beating any records in April, but it was a worthy sacrifice to ensure that I'd still have a cheering squad come race day.

Searching through the assorted plans, presented in an array of tables and PDFs, it became immediately apparent that there are two options to choose from; running to distance or running to time. There seemed to be an even split between the two, with half of the plans specifying the suggested distance for each training run and the other half giving you a suggested time. As I was hoping to come in somewhere around the four-hour mark, opting for a time-based plan that would steadily build me up to that duration seemed to make sense.

With half the field now eliminated, it didn't take me long to settle on a plan and, after browsing those of respected magazines and marathon stalwarts, I came back to the Virgin Money London Marathon website. Its *Intermediate 16-week Schedule* seemed like a good option, not least because Day One was a rest day. So, I downloaded the PDF, pre-populated a Google Calendar with 16 weeks' worth of runs - swapping the odd cross-training session for Wednesday evening badminton - and worked out a start date; 31 December 2018; New Year's Eve...the perfect Rest Day.

The problem now was that it was still September and I had three and a half months to kill before I could kick off the plan I'd spent far too long searching for. Part of me was relieved that I wouldn't need to ramp up my running schedule for a little while yet, but a larger part of me - the same part that, as a child, wanted to open my presents a week before Christmas - felt a little deflated and a lot impatient. I just wanted to get cracking.

My lack of a DeLorean and flux capacitor meant that I had to be patient, all I could do was ensure that I stayed fit and healthy for the rest of the year, maintaining a decent level of fitness and avoiding any unnecessary leg breakages if at all possible. My regular weekly routine of three to four short runs and a long run at the weekend therefore continued and 2018 thankfully wound down without any incidents, illnesses, sprains, breaks or tears.

During that same period of running impatience, however, I had time on my hands to focus on the far scarier prospect of raising £2,000 for Prostate Cancer UK. I had never before had to raise such a significant sum and, because the charity had effectively placed its faith in me to do so, the prospect was daunting. Of course, I knew my fantastic family and friends would help to kick me off, but

I was going to need to do something else to get to the top of my fundraising totaliser.

It also struck me quite early on that my greatest potential asset with this fundraising was my own story. However reluctant I might be to shout about my own health issues, the fact that I defied the odds to get prostate cancer at 40 - and that my life was saved thanks to an NHS health check (that 59 percent of people don't bother to attend) - was surely enough to help me raise money and awareness of the most common cancer in men, especially amongst my own age group.

Up to that point only a handful of friends and family knew much about what I had been through, but if I was going to do this, I was going to have to stick my head above the parapet and tell the world. While both liberating and terrifying in equal measure, I knew what I had to do next...

It was time to make a video.

Chapter 19 - The video

Having begun my career as a journalist and then moved into marketing for charities, I have a fair bit of experience of planning fundraising and awareness campaigns for other people. In the majority of these scenarios, social media has proved vital to the wider promotion and awareness raising potential of campaigns, with video content proving to be the most accessible and popular form of media to spread a message.

Sad as it may be, the days of people stopping to read something online that is more than four words long have passed us by. The proliferation of social media over recent years has also reduced our attention spans, meaning that if something doesn't grab our attention immediately, it's unlikely to hold it for long. There are some exceptions of course, and some forms of social media lend themselves to long form content better than others, but in the majority of social circumstances, content needs to be short, punchy and to the point...or include a cat doing something cute.

After directing countless campaigns from behind the camera, I would therefore have to step in front of it myself if I wanted to share my story, raise awareness of prostate cancer amongst men in their 40s and hopefully boost my fundraising potential. This wasn't a prospect that filled me with joy. I hate the sound of my own voice and fear that I morph into Alan Partridge when the red light comes on, placing the emphasis on the wrong words, not knowing what to do with my hands and looking about as comfortable as the Pope at an Anne Summers party. Nevertheless, it had to be done and the more I thought about it, the more I realised that I actually had an obligation to use this opportunity to make people stop and think.

I know that there are millions of men in their 40s who have never once stopped to think about their prostates. Why would they? It's considered an old man's disease after all. But the majority of men in the UK will have received an invitation upon turning 40 to attend a free NHS health check. So, I had a chance here to create a video and campaign of my own to achieve two primary objectives; firstly, to encourage young men to consider their own prostate health and ask for a PSA test and, secondly, to reinforce the importance of attending NHS health checks. If I failed on the former, but convinced just one man to consider the latter, then that would at least be something.

However, I really didn't want to fail on the former. Since my own experience, I have read much about PSA and, as I discussed in Chapter Six, can appreciate that it is a controversial measure which can on occasion lead to unnecessary treatment. Despite this, I firmly believe that every man should know what his PSA level is, from around the age of 40. It is something that will naturally increase as you get older, but, as I've said already, knowing what your base level is at a young age will give you an indicator of how gradually or steeply your levels have risen over time. This can help to flag cancer early and at least put the power in each man's hands to decide how he wants to move forward. Otherwise, you are simply burying your head in the sand and, heaven forbid, allowing an unknown cancer to grow unchecked inside you.

I am also aware, of course, that a lot of this head burying comes down to pride and/or embarrassment. Men struggle to talk about their penises, prostates and testicles, we put off going to the doctors if we have issues downstairs and prefer to pretend the problems don't exist in the hope that they'll go away by themselves. It is a stigma that, when broken down, is nonsensical in the extreme. Why should one part of our bodies be any different from the rest? It's just skin, bone, flesh and other complicated bits under the surface. Why does it make a difference when the bits we're concerned about are located around the trouser area? And given that the particular pieces of flesh in question are largely responsible for the thing we enjoy doing most of all, why wouldn't you want to ensure that they're in perfect working order? This coupled with the fact that doctors have seen everything, from every angle, inside and out, surely means that the embarrassment factor around attending an appointment with the doctor shouldn't be an issue.

Regardless of the logic though, the fact remains that confronting one's fears and finding the courage to talk to a doctor is a major undertaking for many men. My hope with the fundraising campaign - and ultimately with this book - was to therefore be as honest as I could be about my own experiences, in the hope that others may find the strength to confront their health concerns.

The video I created was a DIY affair, cobbled together on my PC at home, and - although I still cringe when I watch it back - I was pleased with the end result. I chose to speak directly to camera, stressing the importance of NHS health checks and - unashamedly going for the shock factor - how mine had saved my life. I asked men watching to book on to their NHS checks when they were invited to do so and also asked them to donate to Prostate Cancer UK through my JustGiving page in support of my marathon effort. The whole thing took less than a day to film, edit and get online.

My advice to any readers looking to do something similar to support their fundraising is therefore to keep it super simple. You don't need a fancy camera and a degree in television postproduction to edit together a BAFTA-worthy documentary, all you require is a phone or a PC with a decent camera, microphone and some form of editing software.

Don't forget as well that, while sound is hugely important and you should always choose a setting where it doesn't sound like you're talking from inside an empty cathedral, 85 percent of Facebook video is viewed online without sound, so be sure to subtitle your video too (there are a wealth of tools to help you do this). Be honest, open and heartfelt in what you say, make your calls to action clear, don't use licenced music and don't forget to push your fundraising page.

Once complete, the next step is to promote your creation as widely as you can, which is where I hit a small stumbling block with my two-minute piece of self-promotion.

Despite creating my film, excitedly drawing up a marketing and promotion plan and writing the copy to sit alongside a selection of scheduled social media posts to introduce it, actually hitting the 'post' button was far harder than I had anticipated. The issue was that once I did so, the proverbial cat would be out of the bag and there would be no way to get it back in again. Was I ready?

I remember sitting at the computer on that September evening, going through all my Facebook 'friends,' the vast majority of whom I hadn't seen in years, several of whom I don't even remember and many of whom knew nothing of my personal life at all. To them I was Tim, the former colleague, the onetime acquaintance, the chap who I went to that thing with or the guy who I went to school with and wouldn't recognise if I walked past him in the street. Up to that moment in time I was a closed book to them all. I tended to post on Facebook on a decadely basis and when I did it was often so bland and boring that it would have been of no interest to any of them anyway. So, was I ready for them all to know that I had had prostate cancer?

The thought was making me feel unexpectedly nervous, I was giving all these people the chance to gossip and found myself imagining the conversations that might subsequently happen across dinner tables around the country once I'd clicked the button:

"Remember Tim Beynon?"

"No"

"You know, that chap who went to school...tall, skinny, once got knocked out by a cricket bat."

"Ah, yes...why?"

"Well, he's got prostate cancer."

"No way, that's awful."

"I know, who'd have thought it? He always had such a healthy prostate aged 14!"

Okay, well maybe not that last part, but you get my drift. I hated the thought of being the subject of other people's conversations and sympathies, but it was going to have to be a necessary evil if I wanted to raise the £2,000 for Prostate Cancer UK and generate awareness of an issue that might one day affect them too. So, after walking away, having some dinner, mulling it over some more, talking to Alex, going for a run, having a shower, thinking about it some more and then returning to my computer, I hit 'post.'

The reaction I received was totally unexpected.

Chapter 20 - Retweets and surprises

Áfter hitting 'post' and sharing my story with the internet, I sat back and half expected the phone to start ringing, messages to flood into my mobile, emails to ping up on the PC and neighbours to start knocking on the door. Of course, none of that happened and I realised quite quickly that my own inflated ego had just assumed that everyone I knew would be sat with their phone in hand, waiting to respond to a shock announcement from Tim Beynon. In reality, they would see it in time, but they had their own lives to be getting on with and responding to a piece of news from an old school friend or vague acquaintance was probably not that high on their agenda, at least not in the 10 minutes since I posted it.

In the days that followed, however, people did start watching the video and messages gradually started landing in my inbox from the most unexpected of sources. I heard from people I had not seen in person for at least 20 years, each with messages of support and encouragement. My fundraising page, meanwhile, started seeing donations mount up and, as I read each message and as each donation notification pinged up on my phone, I felt increasingly emotional at the impact my video was having.

Some friends wrote at length, while others wrote very little, but said a huge amount with a donation of immense generosity. These were people who were no longer part of my life on a day-to-day basis, but who were part of my life at some point over the past 40 years and for whom a bond of friendship would always remain, regardless of whether or not we were in regular touch. Their kindness and generosity spoke volumes and I will forever be grateful to them for their support.

I was particularly moved by one school friend who wrote a lengthy message explaining how she had fought her own battle with breast cancer, during the same period of time that I had been receiving testing and treatment. Like me, she had faced dark times and she explained with honesty and openness how she had struggled to share news of her diagnosis with others, including her parents. We exchanged messages about the challenges we had both faced, while also reflecting on how far away it all seemed from the days when we would drink cider with friends in a local West Country pub (where the landlord was more than happy to dismiss the small matter of his entire clientele being underage). I was incredibly moved that she had shared so much with me and vowed to keep in touch, certainly more frequently than the once every 20 years it had been up to that point.

Over the days that followed, two other friends also told me of their own experiences with cancer. However, far from being a collection of sob stories and an exchange of bad news, I was uplifted by hearing such honest accounts from people who had once been a part of my life. All had faced up to their situations and got through them, coming out the other side stronger and more appreciative of life. Like me, they had young families and were now getting on with raising their children, grateful for the opportunity to do so thanks to the care they had received. Their generosity, meanwhile, blew me away as I managed to reach the £1,000 mark, just 10 days after posting the video.

My friends and family were of course the first to get my fundraising off the ground and, as grateful as I was to them all, I also knew that I had to try and reach beyond them to the wider world if I was to realise my total and help to raise awareness as far as I could. My marketing plan therefore included reaching out to a few celebrities, a tactic which began to bear fruit - rather spectacularly - in early October 2018 when I was out on a walk in the countryside with my children.

Having enabled notifications for Twitter on my phone I remember climbing a hill on a bright day - holding all the coats, bags and other paraphernalia that my children had offloaded on me five minutes after leaving the house - as my phone began to vibrate repeatedly in my pocket. Assuming it was a call, I took it out - dropping my daughter's favourite hat in the process - and was surprised to see a constant stream of new notifications from total strangers who were all apparently liking a Twitter post in

143

which I was mentioned. Clicking one and opening up Twitter, it became immediately apparent that the King of Twitter himself, his Royal Highness Mr Stephen Fry, had retweeted my video to his 12.6million followers.

Being used to single figure likes and once-in-a-blue-moon comments on my usual Twitter posts, this was new territory for me. My phone was vibrating like a washing machine on spin cycle, trying to keep pace with the incessant notifications. Having been through treatment for prostate cancer himself, Mr Fry had clearly sympathised with my cause and kindly retweeted my original video tweet. The impact was instantaneous as the likes, retweets and comments came within seconds of his post. I had never previously really considered the power of Twitter, but in that moment - on a windswept hill in the middle of nowhere - I was taken aback at the incredible reach one individual can have and what a powerful tool the Twitter machine actually is.

A few years ago, advertisers would have had to spend millions of pounds if they wanted to reach 12 million people across the planet and, before social media, no vehicle for them to do so even existed. TV and radio advertising could reach millions, but not globally, at the same time and for zero cost. Today, however, there are a growing number of social media influencers (I hate that term) who have the power to reach millions of people every day. Of course, how they choose to wield that power is the subject of much debate. Take former President

Trump as a case in point. The once most powerful man on the planet ruled through Twitter, wielding its power to influence the mindset of millions. Many saw his use of Twitter as an abuse of his power, circumventing political protocol and traditional theatres of debate to express his personal opinion on matters of national and international significance. Many others, meanwhile, saw it as a refreshing change to political tradition and took Trump's use of Twitter as a reflection of his status to them as a man of the people, rather than a member of the Washington establishment. Either way, a tweet from Trump could have the power to change the lives of millions, at least until he was banned.

For me though, as the battery on my phone died under the strain of notifications, Twitter - or rather the brilliant Stephen Fry - had put my message in front of millions. It might not have been decrying the failings of the American political system and the alleged theft of a Presidential election, but it was asking the men of the world to take a small bit of action to look after their own wellbeing, so it was all rather humbling.

After the initial deluge of likes had subsided and my phone returned to operating more like a phone and less like a sex toy, I began to receive messages and comments from people I had never met before. These were a mixture of people wishing me luck and those reflecting on the impact that prostate cancer had had on them, their fathers or grandfathers. All were an encouraging sign that I was at least causing people to stop, discuss and reflect, however fleetingly that might be.

This response led me to consider my next move and, after sending a few emails to a few health editors across the national press, *The I* newspaper commissioned me to write a piece on my prostate cancer and how running had helped me through it, with a promise to publish a link to my JustGiving page alongside it. The fee went straight to my fundraising pot and the double-page article was subsequently published in early 2019, in the build up to the marathon. Once again, the feedback I received from friends, family and strangers was incredible. One woman wrote to me through my JustGiving page to say that she had sent the article to her son who had recently been diagnosed with prostate cancer and was struggling to come to terms with the prospect of treatment and the potential impact on his lifestyle. Her son, a fortnight later, also donated and wrote to me to say that the article had inspired him to think differently about his diagnosis, to talk to Prostate Cancer UK and to exercise more as a way to distract himself from negative thoughts about the future.

At that point, I really felt for the first time that I had achieved something with this small piece of campaigning, both for myself and for the chap who had written to me. He was, I hoped, able to relate to what I had written and take something positive from it. I, meanwhile, was feeling a warm sense of satisfaction at the thought that I had made a difference to someone I had never met. My anxiety over letting the cat out of the bag and sharing my story with the world had also now completely dissipated and I had no qualms whatsoever about talking to whoever would listen about my own experiences, gloved fingers and all.

146

As I have found with writing this book, the act of putting pen to paper - or fingers to keyboard - was also incredibly cathartic. Whereas I had struggled to talk to many people about all that I had been through, it was immeasurably easier to write about it all. Any psychotherapists reading this will undoubtedly be feverishly putting pen to paper themselves at this point, but regardless of my shortcomings in regard to face-to-face communications, I felt unburdened by the process of translating my own story into prose. The fact that it could end up being read by those very people I had failed to talk to - as well as countless strangers - was ironic, but still a hell of a lot easier than picking up the phone and trying to explain to friends how I had been feeling for the past few months.

This intense period of fundraising and self-promotion had also served to quickly while away the three months between securing a place in the Marathon and commencing my carefully chosen 16-week training plan. By the time I got to the end of 2018 - almost a year to the day since receiving my diagnosis - I had raised the £2,000 I needed for Prostate Cancer UK, I had helped to raise awareness in regard to NHS health checks and PSA tests, and I had managed to avoid breaking my legs. So, going into 2019, I was in a good place and ready to begin training for the Virgin Money London Marathon in just four months' time...after my designated New Year's Eve rest day of course.

147

Chapter 21 - Training gets underway

Thankfully, I am boring.

And being boring meant that New Year's Eve 2018 did not go down in history as the most raucous of affairs in the Beynon household. The agenda for the day involved a trip to a garden centre to buy two goldfish, a family game of Scrabble, a solitary beer and bed - approximately 10 minutes after watching the midnight fireworks. My 20-year-old self would have been appalled, but my 41-year-old self absolutely loved it.

The party-free day meant that I would start 2019 hangover free and - rather than monging in front of the TV and eventually dragging my reluctant body out for an enforced walk with an equally reluctant family - I could look forward to the first training run of my carefully selected 16-week marathon training programme.

As it happens, run number one was an 'easy 20-minute run' - hardly a gruelling start to training, but a milestone nonetheless. I chose a familiar road-based 5K route and cut it short towards the end as there was no chance of completing the full circuit in my allotted time, at least not at an 'easy' pace. Stopping my watch and cooling down, it hardly felt like I had done anything, but at the same time I knew that it represented the start of a journey that would ramp up in intensity quite quickly.

From that gentle starting point, I would be running four times a week, every week, building up time on my feet during the shorter weekday runs and extending it further with each long run at the weekend. This was to be the focus for the first six weeks of the programme, before higher intensity tempo and threshold sessions joined the party.

During those early weeks, it was predominantly about building stamina and getting used to running with increased frequency. However, I was also aware that my lack of cross training and reluctance to go anywhere near a gym had - for quite some time - left me with laughably little core strength. A desk job, regular back ache and fear of lifting anything heavier than an envelope is testament to this. I was like a human Wheat Crunchie - no core, likely to crack under pressure and occasionally rather odd smelling, so something had to be done.

I knew that a significant increase in running was also likely to significantly increase my risk of injury and that one way to reduce that risk was to build up some core strength. Still reluctant to enter a gym, the simplest way for me to do so was therefore to set myself a plank challenge.

On paper, this was my kind of challenge, it involved no equipment, could be done in pyjamas and took a matter of minutes to complete. In reality, of course, the plank is a beast of a challenge. It freezes time for its unwitting participants, turning every painful second into an hour and causing challengers to shake uncontrollably as they inevitably crumble while attempting to hold the simple position for the allotted time. For onlookers, at least, it provides a few minutes of comedic relief as the planker collapses on the floor, declaring themselves utterly spent after just a minute or two's effort. Weightlifting aside, there are few other physical activities that last such a short amount of time (insert your own joke/snigger here).

On day three of training, I therefore decided to introduce a daily plank challenge, starting at a minute and adding 10 seconds every day until I got to five minutes. Again, I naively thought that this would be an easy addition to my programme and, for the first few days, it wasn't too bad. Approaching one minute and thirty seconds, however, I realised that this was going to be tougher than anticipated. My feeble core was turning me into a quivering wreck at the end of each plank and, although my children found this hilarious, it made me realise further how much work I had ahead of me to build up a set of muscles that had essentially been ignored for 41 years. My competitive streak, meanwhile, was committed to getting to five minutes, purely to prove my scoffing offspring wrong.

Planking became a part of my daily routine, carried out before work and somewhere between breakfast and teeth brushing. I would assume the position - usually in the bedroom - and the rest of the family would carry on the school-run preparations around me.

"Dad, have you seen my PE kit?"

"No, don't...talk....to...me."

"Dad, Molly punched me!"

"Good, carry on."

"Dad, you know in Star Wars...what happens to Obi Wan Kenobe's body when Darth Vader kills him? Why isn't there any blood? Where does his body go? Dad? Do you know? Dad? Dad? Daaaaaad?"

"GO...AWAY....5...more....s..e...c...o...n.....d....s!" [COLLAPSE]

"Forget it, I'll Google it."

And so it continued, day after day. However, while undoubtedly both a physical and mental challenge that you look forward to about as much as stepping barefoot on Lego, planking is at least a pastime that delivers results quickly. Indeed, it doesn't take long to progress from a one-minute planker to a three or four minute planker and the results are tangible. Once you've planked for a little while, you do feel stronger and it does interestingly correlate with the increased effort you're putting into running. While difficult to separate the two, there's no doubt that a stronger core does help to push your marathon training along, and I'm sure there's plenty of science out there to back that up.

Indeed, according to Livestrong*, benefits of planking include better core stability, better posture, strong and stable shoulders, improved muscle endurance and stronger glutes. In other words, a total upper body and bum workout. As someone who regularly moans of lower back pain, stiff shoulders and neck ache - undoubtedly brought about through prolonged desk work - planking could be the answer. If it gives me a Brad Pitt arse to boot, bonus!

The mental benefits of planking are also worthy of note. Every day, without fail, the additional 10 seconds feels like the most painful hour of your life. Every day, at about three or four seconds into the 10, you're convinced you're not going to make it to the end. By seven or eight seconds, however, you're pretty sure you will and by nine seconds you're over the moon that you're going to get there. The elation at conquering your additional daily seconds is a genuine high and sets you up for the rest of the day, at least until the kids start complaining that they can't find their shoes and you find yourself scrambling to get them out of the door in time to get to school. Of course, the thought of adding another 10 seconds to that time tomorrow also seems absurd.

One other unexpected consequence of those early training weeks was the increased amount of kit-washing required. Running four times a week meant that the turnover of running-related laundry increased significantly, with assorted shorts, leggings, t-shirts and compression socks regularly found hanging off radiators throughout the house during the winter months, often relegating non-essential items (regular underwear, school uniform, work shirts etc.) to non-heated drying points. Investment in additional kit was eventually required to reduce the washing machine usage, but the ratio of running to non-running-related washing was heavily skewed towards the former on the majority of wash loads, especially given the fact that Alex is also a regular runner. The mixing up of socks, shorts and sports bras was also therefore a regular occurrence, with my wife often having to scrabble around in my kit draw for the bra I'd inadvertently thought was my knee brace.

It was therefore no surprise that by the end of the first month of marathon training, I had a dedicated running kit drawer and a growing shopping list.

Over the training weeks that followed, my running-related purchases began to mount up, with the most expensive addition coming courtesy of a visit to a local running-specialist shop for new trainers. This experience, if you've never been, is one to savour for runners who like to think of themselves as serious. For me - as someone who usually enjoys shopping about as much as colonic irrigation - it was my second visit and I walked in with, I like to think, the air of someone who knows a thing or two about running. I felt like a regular, a professional who knew the lay of the land and what to expect from the gait analysis and trainer option conversation that was about to commence. In reality, I suspect, I was a regular lamb to the slaughter once again, a gullible amateur runner who the savvy sales folk knew would lap up the chance to see himself running in slow motion on a treadmill, while being told he was supinating or pronating (look it up) to one degree or another. The mark (me) would then be shown a selection of top end trainers and have his ego massaged further by the ever-friendly salesman who would carefully explain why these particular £130 trainers would suit his specific running style. Mission accomplished, the mark would hand over his cash and leave feeling like he had spent wisely after a wonderful, personalised and professional experience.

Despite being aware of all of this, I fell for it all once again and relished the opportunity to try on various pairs of Asics, Hokas and Brooks, test driving them all on the store's hard-working treadmill. Yes, there's a large degree of sales patter, but it does genuinely make you feel like you are a bit special. You also wouldn't buy a car without test driving it first, so why should it be any different with trainers. They are the vehicle via which you will travel around 500 miles - 26.2 of which, for me, would be in London - so ensuring that they are comfortable and at least capable of reducing the risk of injury is important. Although, having said that, there's no point in buying a Ferrari when a decent Ford will do the job.

The running shop experience is also the closest I will ever get to having a personal shopper. In no other aspect of my life would I enter a shop and expect to try everything first and have assorted people tend to my every need before finalising my purchases. I may, however, try this approach the next time I go to Tesco, but I somehow doubt the Manager will look favourably on me if I was to cook up a sirloin and chips in Aisle 4 before deciding I didn't really like it and opting for a piece of salmon - wrapped nicely for me by an attentive fish expert - instead.

The frugal spendthrift inside me, however, is never far away and, although I relished the experience of being sat on a posh bench, surrounded by boxes of trainers that I had nonchalantly waved away like a medieval king, I did Google the ones that I had finally chosen. Unsurprisingly I found that they were £20 cheaper on Amazon but the store, to their immense credit, had no issue with this and honoured the Amazon price.

So at the end of the day, I still left the running shop substantially worse off than when I went in, but richer for the experience. My trainer of choice in the end was a pair of Brooks Ghosts 12s, which I hoped would help me to build up the miles and fend off any injuries.

*https://www.livestrong.com/article/500440-what-does-the-plank-exercise-benefit/

Chapter 22 - Injuries and niggles

I never used to be the kind of person to moan about aches and pains, largely because I don't think I ever used to get aches and pains. At least, as a younger man, the only times I used to moan about my body were when I had done something genuinely worthy of moaning about; breaking my arm aged 10, falling off a ski lift aged 27, playing football against a team of teenagers aged 32, hangovers up to the age of 40 and other such ill-judged misdemeanors. Getting out of bed and rising from a seated position never used to be an issue.

Over recent years, however, moaning seems to have become a major part of my waking day. Most mornings I now arise (slowly and with some effort) with at least one new niggle to worry about, going on to spend most of the first hour of the day discussing its possible causes and consequences with Alex.

I have no idea how it is even possible to wake in the morning with a knee sprain? What could I possibly have done while fully reclined and asleep that would lead to a lower limb injury? Do I sleepwalk/run or rock climb?

What other explanation could there be for an unconscious human being to amass nightly injuries?

However they are obtained, the results seem real enough as I regularly limp downstairs in the morning complaining of a sore calf, painful hip, aching joints, diminishing eyesight, lower back stiffness or headache. Granted most of my morning ailments clear up with a cup of tea, but this age-induced phenomenon has also meant that I now feel more susceptible than ever to running-related injuries.

I am also well aware that I don't help myself at all by routinely failing to warm up, cool down or stretch properly and that an hour of badminton once a week is the sum total of my cross-training regime. I should be doing all these things with gusto on a regular basis, as the magazines, YouTube videos and much-fitter friends keep telling me. The issue I have is that I am fundamentally lazy and that running is really the only form of exercise that I truly enjoy. Give me the choice between a half-hour virtual pilates class or the PS4 and I'll be logging into FIFA21 faster than you can say; "take a deep breath."

Of course, I know that all these peripheral undertakings are good for me, that they will strengthen the areas that need strengthening, protect me from injury and help me to cut down on the self-pitying protestations that even my children are now bored of. But finding the motivation to do them is so hard, even when training for the Marathon. The fear of injury was reason enough to pay closer attention than normal to the extracurricular activities that accompany running, but a misplaced assumption that 'it'll be ok to skip stretching, just this once,' meant that I continued to neglect these fundamentals. Nevertheless, the prospect of picking up a sprain, pulling a hamstring, twisting a knee or rolling an ankle at any point along the 16-week journey was terrifying, and increasingly so as the days and weeks passed by. The closer it got to Marathon day, the more there was to lose from a silly injury, so while the training load increased and my body felt like it was being pushed harder, the more aware I had to be of the hints and signals of potential issues.

Unfortunately, as my wife can evidence - through 16 years of spectacularly ill-judged birthday and Christmas presents - I have never been very good at either yoga or picking up on signals of any kind.

And the same is unfortunately the case when it comes to listening to my own body. Six weeks into my training and I found myself noticing a recurring pain in my left hip, at roughly the same two-hour mark during my long runs. Assuming it was just a little bit of muscle tiredness or cramp, I would stop, stretch and carry on, but after a further couple of weeks, it seemed to be getting worse and I found myself picking up the phone to book myself in for a probably long overdue appointment with the physio.

Up to that point I had been in denial that I had a problem and was hoping that my hip would miraculously heal itself, while simultaneously allowing me to continue to increase the intensity and duration of my weekly running, with zero cross or strength training. I knew it was illogical and pretty much impossible, but I went into it with the same blind hope that sometimes clouds my judgement in other areas of my life, such as when my car develops a strange noise and I turn the radio up in order to block out the prospect of a costly trip to the garage. But at the end of the day, there's no escaping the truth, which is exactly why the nation's mechanics and physios remain in business.

So, a few days later I found myself on the physio's bench being roughly handled by a man I'd met a mere matter of minutes before. Like taking the car to the garage, there followed a degree of breathing in through teeth, some concerned mumblings and then a protracted technical explanation of the precise issue, which I pretended to understand with some carefully timed nods of the head. In short, I had managed to develop iliotibial band syndrome that was manifesting itself in my hip and would certainly not get better by itself. I would require repeat £50-a-time visits to the physio (at which point I swear I saw my assailant stifling a grin), an immediate reduction in training load and an equally immediate commencement of hip and core-related exercises. With a half marathon a matter of three weeks away, I was worried.

Kicking myself that I didn't head to the physio or start squatting my way around the house sooner, I was now facing the prospect of having to go 'off plan' for a few weeks. Despite having convinced myself at the very beginning of the training that I needed a plan that would allow for flexibility to accommodate the unpredictable elements of fatherhood and life, I had actually stuck to its schedule with anal devotion. Up to that point, I had not missed a session or altered a single training instruction. I had become at one with my training plan, changing the rest of my life to fit around it and obeying its command regardless of weather conditions, work or family commitments or, as it transpires, iliotibial annoyances. But now, on the orders of a man to whom I had paid a small fortune in order to effectively be tortured for an hour, I was going to have to stop it in its tracks, and the prospect terrified me.

Armed with a set of instructions and daily exercises to, hopefully, get me to the start line of the half marathon that was integral to my marathon training, I left the physio despondent, but mentally committed to sticking rigidly to my new recovery programme. This would mean twice daily stretching and hip-specific exercises, most of which involved either lying on my back or leaning against a wall and raising my leg. On paper, both sounded fairly straight forward. In practice, I was taken aback at how challenging they were and, once again, at how feeble my core strength was.

Despite my consistent planking I found myself shaking while attempting multiple reps across the different hip-lift exercises. Alex, who runs less, but regularly enjoys yoga, lay beside me on occasion and put my feeble attempts to shame. Whereas she could hold the pelvic lifts with enough stability to balance a tennis ball on her stomach, I was shaking around like I was attempting the exercise while drunk at sea. There was no wonder my iliotibial band had kicked up a fuss, it was effectively acting like a rubber band trying to hold together my jelly pelvis.

All this stretching and pelvis-related balancing momentarily distracted me from the fact that I would be off-plan for at least a couple of weeks. After Googling the impact of this enforced hiatus on my marathon preparedness, I was reassured by the general consensus that two weeks would not see me falling short of the 26.2 miles on race day. However, this did nothing to stem my growing sense of frustration at not being able to complete the speed sessions, hill sessions and long runs that I had plotted out on my training calendar. Lying on my back and lifting my bum off the floor for 10 minutes was a poor replacement for smashing out 15 miles on the canal towpath.

Unsurprisingly I have never been the most patient of people. Indeed, the fact that our home is essentially filled with an array of impulse purchases is testament to this particular characteristic, together with my often single-minded determination to see things through to completion.

Exhibit A: FooBot - A high-tech air quality monitor

Having read an article somewhere about the dangers of household chemical pollutants and volatile airborne compounds, I set about researching the best way to keep my family safe from these invisible killers through the purchase of some kind of device to add to my collection of smoke alarms and carbon monoxide detectors. The result was the purchase of a high-tech digital air monitor with accompanying smart phone app that, ever since it's been turned on, has basically just confirmed that the air in my house is absolutely fine and that I wasted my money. The only volatile compounds in our immediate atmosphere, it turns out, emanate from my son.

Nevertheless, despite my impatience, I stuck to the programme and saw out the fortnight of pelvic nursing, returning to the physio for a hopeful green light three days before the Fleet Half Marathon. After a further period of pulling, poking and painful massage, however, the muscle torturer gave me a rather non-committal amber light.

"Well, you could, but, well, it's probably not a good idea."

Which, of course, I took to mean: "Green light Mr Beynon, away you go!"

So, after handing over more money and essentially committing to ignore the advice that had just cost me £50, I left determined to take part in the weekend's forthcoming half marathon.

Of course, this was silly, but the fact was that the physio's advice - and my hard-fought adherence to his programme - was actually bearing fruit. My hip was feeling stronger and I was running more or less pain free. I hadn't clocked up anything near a half marathon distance in the preceding fortnight, but the rest and the hard work on the floor had surely done me good.

Psychologically, I felt that taking part in the Fleet Half Marathon was an important milestone on my journey to the London Marathon start line. It was part of the training plan and therefore an integral part of the whole experience. Also, it had cost me £27, so I was determined to get my money's worth!

162

Chapter 23 - The Fleet Half

O n a crisp, dry and overcast Sunday morning in March 2019 - a little over a month before I would hopefully be nervously waiting for the start of the London Marathon - I found myself nervously waiting for the start of the Fleet Half Marathon.

My local event, the Fleet Half is the highlight of the running calendar in my neck of the woods. An always well attended occasion that slots neatly into the training plans for anyone running in the Capital a few weeks later, it comprises of a mostly flat course that meanders its way around the streets of Fleet before plunging into the nearby countryside and returning to a finish area in the town's sprawling Calthorpe Park.

The added bonus of being able to walk to the start from home was in stark contrast to the early morning train and tube adventures that lay ahead of me to get to Blackheath in April, so I took full advantage and ensured I had plenty of time for a decent breakfast and a warmup walk/jog to the start line.

Now, I have taken part in plenty of races over the years and would like to go so far as to say that I am experienced in the routines of race preparedness, namely;

1. Check the weather and set your kit out the night before.
2. Don't run the race in anything you haven't worn already in training and...
3. Make sure you do a poo before you leave the house!

However, as I prepared to leave the house, the usual ridiculous pre-race uncertainties kicked in, namely:

1. Can I trust the weather forecast, is it really going to stay dry? The app says a one percent chance of rain, but that one percent could be torrential. Should I take that rain jacket for the pre-race wait?
2. I've got some nice new running socks that I haven't tried out yet, surely they'd be good for race day?
3. I've fulfilled my No.2 quota for the morning, but have I miscounted?

The result, as usual, is that I leave the house - after pointlessly sitting on the loo for 10 minutes - with much more stuff than I will ever need for the few hours I am to be outside. In reality, I literally need nothing more than the clothes I am wearing, but yet again I found myself carrying a drawstring bag with jumper, jacket, post-race snacks and enough gels to run an ultra with. I knew that 99 percent of the bag's contents would be returning home untouched, but still I found myself walking to the race with it on my back.

Also on my back was my trusty drinks bladder, full of an isotonic concoction that I had been using for a while. It tasted like the kind of Ribena your gran used to make, when she took dilution to essentially mean a 50/50 split between cordial and water. It was worryingly sweet, but definitely packed a punch and, I felt, was performance enhancing - although obviously not in a Lance Armstrong sense.

As ever on race days, I was surprised at how few people use water bladders or bring their own drinks to the events they've been training for. Surely being familiar with the liquid you are consuming - and being able to consume it in an easy manner - is preferable to having to grab a bottle or cup from a soaked volunteer and wrestle with the lid before inadvertently giving yourself a shower while trying to quench your thirst on the go.

Of course, I understand that running events are expensive these days, but are runners really that desperate to get their money's worth that they have to consume as many free drinks as they can on the way round? And why don't organisers scrap water stops altogether for that matter? Every runner taking part has managed to train without relying on cub scouts to hand them water every three miles, so why not encourage runners to bring their own drinks and lop a tenner off the entry fee? Cheaper for runners, better for the environment, simpler events for organisers...seems to make sense to me.

165

The other common pre-race practice that has always slightly baffled me is runners' sudden and inexplicable desire to warm up with more enthusiasm than they have ever warmed up before. This was certainly the case as I made my way to the starting area and after handing in my almost suitcase of non-essentials at the bag drop. All around me, hopping, high-knee running, sprinting, butt-kicking and stretching was taking place as the expansive holding field was criss-crossed by nervous runners warming up more than any of them had ever warmed up before.

Every individual was also trying to portray an image of seasoned running professionalism, unconsciously saying to themselves and all those around them:

"I am warming up. I always warm up. This is my regular warm-up routine. I always perform at least 20 varied pre-run exercises before every run. I just need to ensure that everyone around me can see that this is my usual routine and that I am taking this race extremely seriously. I'm not going to fall foul of a torn hamstring within the first kilometre, so I'm going to zig zag across this field a hundred times and clock up the best part of 5km before I even start."

In reality, of course, none of the 200 folks currently grapevining across the football pitch has ever done more than jog on the spot for the 30 seconds it takes their watch to find a GPS signal. But today is race day and the thing about these occasions is that, despite an awareness of the ridiculousness of the 30-minute warm-up, the peer pressure factor kicks in and even the most sceptical of runners soon finds himself jogging up and down the touchline with a look of earned concentration. I was no different.

With half an hour to go until we were to be called to the start line, I found myself warming up with the masses, finding the obligatory lamppost to stretch out calf muscles that didn't really need stretching and adding a few thousand unnecessary steps to my daily count. By the time the PA system asked us to make our way to the start, I felt warm and ready to go, while a couple of the more extreme warmer-upperers looked like they'd already completed the course.

As ever, there then followed what seemed like a painfully long wait for the actual start of the race. I was so far down the road that I couldn't even see the front runners, but as I waited, surrounded by people who all seemed to be running in pairs or groups, my thoughts turned for the first time to my still recovering hip and the words of my physio. Was this really a good idea?

Waiting to begin a 13.1-mile race, I was suddenly having second thoughts. What if I did myself some serious damage and put my London hopes in jeopardy? What's more, I'd probably just notched up a completely unintentional additional mile and a half while warming up. I wondered whether any of the other excited runners around me had been to the physio three days earlier and advised not to run. I suspected not.

Ahead, I heard a far-off claxon and could see the sea of colour slowly moving, like a dam of technicolor water

167

having suddenly been released. A minute or so later I found myself gently jogging towards the official start and the timing mats. Our pace picked up and, before we knew it, we were underway.

It was at this point that I made the decision not to race. I would run at an easy pace and complete the course, but I was not going to push it at all. However, it turns out this is not as easy as it sounds.

When all those around you are clearly running to achieve a certain time or to beat a personal best and therefore streaming past you, your every instinct is to push harder, to go that little bit faster than you have done in training and allow yourself to be swept up in the adrenalin of the day. Voluntarily choosing not to do so means fighting a basic human instinct and sacrificing competitiveness for completion. Like not bothering to swim when you're out of your depth or not filling your plate when presented with a free buffet, it feels completely wrong.

Nevertheless, I glanced at my watch, settled on a pace of around 5.40 a kilometre and tried to suppress the urge to go faster. Also attempting some complex mental maths as I went, I calculated that this pace would bring me home more or less bang on, if not a touch under, two hours. That was at least something as I've always thought of the two-hour threshold for a half marathon as a psychological hurdle. Under and you can count it as a success, over and something's gone wrong. So, if I wasn't going to race it, I could at least make sure I came home in under two hours. At least that was the mental plan I formed in my mind as I saw out the first few kilometres through Fleet town centre.

Maintaining my consistently mediocre pace as the race went on, I settled into it, treating it more like a Sunday long run than a race and began to enjoy the experience as the route took us along familiar local roads that I would never normally run along. Diving into the Hampshire countryside and through local villages with picture postcard houses, cheering locals and children with tubs of jelly babies, I was reminded why running is so life affirming. Here I was, a little over a year after major cancer surgery, back to almost full fitness - dodgy hip aside - and feeling more alive than I had done in a long time.

This was the first competitive event I had taken part in since parting ways with my prostate and, as each mile passed, I made sure to take in the cheers, chants and 'Go Daddy' posters that lined the parts of the route that passed through populated areas. I made sure to thank the volunteers marshalling roads, pointing the way, reminding folks not to wear earphones and clapping continuously. I high-fived children with the kind of careless abandon we did before Covid-19 and I exchanged occasional pleasantries with my fellow runners, no doubt causing them to wonder why I was running with a broad grin rather than the usual look of pained determination that befits those actually competing for a time.

At one point, around 10 miles in, I found myself following a man of similar age, although more of a Mike Tindall to my Peter Crouch in regard to physique, who I noticed was also running with an injury. The reason I could tell was that he had taped 90 percent of his left leg with assorted strips of kinesiology tape. So substantial was the patchwork of multicoloured tape, in fact, that I couldn't tell whether the affected joint of the offending limb was the ankle, knee or hip. Indeed, judging by the technical nature of the criss-crossing tape, I assumed that his entire leg had been shattered in some kind of a freak accident and was now being held together in much the same way that large portions of my house are held together by gaffer tape.

Allowing myself a chuckle at my fellow competitor's liberal application of the magic tape, I felt like giving him a high five and a slap on the back as I edged past - out of respect for his determination to tackle the day's race despite his obvious anxiety over his lower limb's match fitness. However, being British - and also because I was worried that any physical contact might actually see him turn to dust - I didn't say a word and continued on my way towards the finish.

With three miles to go, I was still on track to finish in just under two hours. However, between that point and around 500 metres from the timing mats, I must have got distracted - possibly from looking out for my own family who weren't in the pre-arranged waving spot at which I had expected to see them. The result was that, after waving at someone I vaguely knew from the school run, I glanced at my watch to discover that I had a little over two minutes to get to the end if I wanted to see the number one at the front of my finishing time. Panic set in.

Having religiously stuck to the same pace for 12.6 miles, I was going to have to pretty much sprint the last 500 metres, which my hip was telling was a very bad idea. Ignoring this, I turned it up a few gears and set my sights on the finish, treating the end of the race like a 400-metre track session. The result, to anyone looking on from the packed pavements, was the sight of a slightly deranged looking guy weaving through tired runners, like a commuter fighting fellow rush hour commuters to catch the train he's already late for.

It was all a bit sad, a bit late and ultimately a bit fruitless. I crossed the line in two hours and 15 seconds.

On reflection, however, and as I chomped my way through the obligatory post-race banana, I wasn't that bothered. I had enjoyed the race, my hip had held out, I wasn't feeling too tired and I knew that - with a month to go - I was in good shape for London. Although I might have to buy myself some kinesiology tape for the big day, just in case.

Chapter 24 - Taper time

With the half marathon behind me, the countdown to London was really under way. All that now lay between me and Blackheath was the small matter of my three longest training runs; 27km, 30km and 37km, or as I was seeing them; 2 hours 45 mins, 3 hours and, finally, 3 hours 30 minutes. With under a month to go I had found that running to time rather than distance was really helping me to get my head around the challenge of my weekend long runs. It was also helping my family, meanwhile, to plan lunch around my training.

Being out for such large chunks of Sunday does play havoc with family life. With two young children - aged eight and seven at the time - opting out of the standard weekend carnage in favour of some blissfully selfish me time, meant that parenting duties fell exclusively to Alex, who was already doing the lion's share on a weekday basis. By training to time, however, I could at least give her a decent estimate as to how long I would be shirking my fatherly responsibilities for each Sunday.

Of course, the issue when training runs are around the three-hour mark is that even an estimation of your likely return time cannot do much to change the fact that your chances of winning the *Sunday Afternoon Father of The Day* award are slim, due to the fact that you are absolutely knackered.

The feeling of guilt was absolute as I approached the closing weeks of the marathon training plan. Our Sundays were totally dominated by my running and my children had to subsequently endure a father whose enthusiasm for garden football and impromptu games of 'tag' was at an all-time low. Anyone watching who may not have been aware of my morning's activities, must surely have assumed that I was the world's laziest parent. Presented with two hyperactive bundles of love and excitement who wanted nothing more than for their Dad to chase them around the garden, there I was lolloping around like a Duracell Bunny on two almost dead Poundland value batteries.

Alex, meanwhile, had to put up with a husband who just moaned about tired legs and occasional blisters, and for whom undertaking such necessary duties as fixing the ever-dripping guttering was always a mission impossible. In short, I was useless. Well, more useless than usual.

This uselessness reached its peak in the month before London when my Sundays were taken up with increasingly lengthy runs, each in turn becoming the longest distance I had ever run. The first, a mere two hours and 45 minutes, actually started with a Junior Parkrun.

173

Lining up on the start line of our local Parkrun for little people, the plan was that I would use this as a warm-up with the children, helping them around the 2km course and enjoying some quality time before parting ways and heading off on a circuitous route that would take me on a mixture of trail and road, up and down a few familiar hills and eventually home. The reality, of course, was that I looked like the most over prepared runner in Junior Parkrun history.

As I warmed up with the assembled mass of enthusiastic youngsters and hungover parents, I was clearly the only adult in attendance - perhaps the only adult ever - to do so while sporting a hydration vest and compression socks. Either those parents casting sideways glances at me were unfamiliar with the course and wondering whether they had spectacularly underestimated the grueling 2km that lay ahead, or, as was more likely, they had placed me in the 'pushy parent/show off' camp, alongside the one other standout dad who'd taken himself off to stretch in isolation in the middle of the park.

Even my children looked embarrassed.

Regardless, I embraced my pushy parent status and cheered on my kids as we made our way around the course. My appearance clearly had the desired effect on my son as he sped up in order to distance himself from me and subsequently claimed a personal best. In fact, so significant was his new time, that I may employ similar techniques in regard to encouraging performance leaps into the future; assorted fancy dress, exaggerated displays of parental affection in front of his friends, singing while running, the embarrassment list is endless.

Having successfully humiliated my offspring, I waved them goodbye - or rather, I waved and they sulked - and headed off on the first of my last three long runs. Perhaps as a result of the previous weekend's half marathon, I found the kilometres slow going and hard on the legs. I was averaging in the six-minute kilometres, rather than my more familiar five-minute-somethings and spent the duration feeling like I was fighting for energy, especially on the seemingly relentless hills.

Once home, showered and uploaded to Strava, I chalked it down as one to forget, a bad run that didn't deserve to be dwelled on.

However, I did dwell on it and it began to play on my mind. Why was I so slow? Why did it feel so hard? What if it felt like that throughout the Marathon? How was I going to finish?

On reflection, it was no coincidence that this tough run had come a few days before one of my routine three-monthly PSA blood tests. As ever, I had pushed the prospect of another test to the back of my mind, instead choosing to focus on running and all that lay ahead of me with the forthcoming marathon. However, sometimes there is no hiding from reality. The stress of three-monthly blood tests to find out whether my PSA level was still undetectable was always there, especially in the fortnight before each test and in the week afterwards as I waited for the results.

After a radical prostatectomy - even with a positive prognosis - it is still necessary to undergo regular testing to make sure that your cancer has not returned. For me, I could take a degree of comfort from the fact that the pathology of my extracted prostate had concluded that my tumour had been contained within it, but not even the most experienced consultant can 100 percent guarantee that it won't come back. So, testing continues, every three months, to measure PSA levels. An undetectable level means that you are still in remission and technically cancer free, but even a slight increase could mean that your cancer has returned.

Even today, as I write this and after my tests have moved to six-monthly, I struggle to describe how all-consuming and overwhelming this worry is. It never gets any easier either. The passing of time provides no reassurance. I have read enough stories of men whose cancer returned five, six, seven or more years after surgery, to make me realise that this is going to be with me forever. Like wearing the heaviest of coats and living within a storm cloud, the fear combines with lethargy, anger and short-temperedness to turn me into a self-consumed monster for a few weeks. I am aware of it. I hate it. But there's nothing I can do about it at all. Until the phone rings.

Once I get the call - "great news Mr Beynon, your PSA level remains undetectable" - the clouds lift, the sun comes out, I feel lighter, the fear disappears and I return to normal life. The coat gets packed away and I get on with living a normal life, forgetting for now that I'll have to go through the whole thing again in a few months' time.

176

So, my disappointing long run, on that Parkrun morning, was probably as much to do with the state of my head as it was to do with the state of my legs. Although I cannot remember actively contemplating my cancer fate on the run itself, the closeted worry was still there and, I believe, played its part in slowing me down and making me feel generally rubbish. This entirely non-clinical theory certainly played out the following week as, two days after receiving the positive phone call I had been longing for, I set out on my penultimate long run, the three-hour benchmark.

Having regretted the hilly runs the preceding week, I opted for the flattest three hours I could and headed for the local canal towpath. For anyone who has ever run along any stretch of Britain's 2,000+ mile canal network, the experience is nothing short of joyous. Peaceful and serene, the canal changes with the seasons, but is always a place of calm and beauty. Requiring no navigation whatsoever, it is also impossible to get lost on a canal towpath and therefore runs along its twists and turns are devoid of the mental route calculations usually needed for road or trail running. With only a handful of weeks to go until the sensory overload that would be the London Marathon, spending three hours in the company of the occasional fisherman, dog walker and assorted water-based wildlife was exactly what I needed.

My mindset going into this three-hour waterside adventure was also completely different. I set off looking forward to what lay ahead and wondering how far along the canal I would get before about turning at 1.5 hours and heading home. The sun was also shining, there was a feeling of Spring in the air and I had a new audiobook to listen to en route, all was well with the world.

The fact that the dark shadow of cancer testing had lifted also meant that my legs felt lighter and my energy levels were higher than the same time a week earlier. The physiological impact of good news was tangible. I wanted to run, I felt good and the thought of three hours on my feet didn't faze me.

What followed was therefore an enjoyable exercise in pacing, fisherman avoidance and heron spotting as I made my way north along the canal towards Basingstoke. Passing picturesque canal-side properties with lovingly kept miniature quays, occupied by moored boats with Tolkien-esque names, like Misty, Willow and Merlin, I wallowed in the tranquility and the chocolate-box Britishness of it all.

My Fitbit watch, however, decided that it simply couldn't be bothered with recording the day's run with any sense of accuracy, instead choosing to stop and start at will, cutting off entire sections of the canal and frustrating me with assorted beeps and vibrations as it attempted to lock on to a GPS signal. So, although I ended the day with a route map on Strava that looked more like a line graph than a canal route, I returned home feeling relatively comfortable and with renewed confidence for the Marathon.

Over the week that followed I settled on a return to the canal path for the three and a half hour long run that would mark the end of the Sunday full morning sessions and also decided to use the experience to test my race day nutrition strategy.

By strategy, of course, I meant the vague plan I had to wing it in regard to what I was going to eat and drink over the duration of the Marathon. While I had spent weeks practicing how I was going to move my legs and feet, I had spent relatively little time thinking about how I was going to power my lower limbs over the 26.2 miles. In terms of fluids, I had settled on the isotonic powdered drink from Decathlon for my shorter runs that seemed to have done the trick, providing a much-needed glucose hit to keep tiredness at bay. However, once the mileage had increased enough to require a more substantial dose of carbohydrates, I moved on to gels. Having only rarely used them before, I had never been much of a fan and had struggled to hold down the ridiculously expensive supplements after squeezing them down my throat. The experience had always felt like attempting to eat room temperature school custard while running, occasionally triggering my gag reflex or leaving me with stomach cramps.

However, it transpires that not all gels are the same and after trying several different versions of the vomit pouches, I settled on one that I could at least keep down and which didn't leave me feeling like I would shortly need to dive into the nearest bush for an emergency poo. While the assorted flavours on offer all tasted of mildly different types of sick, they did actually seem to work and, when taken at half-hourly intervals, seemed to effectively keep tiredness at bay. The only issue with this frequency of consumption, on the long runs, was that opening and squeezing several gels would always result in sticky fingers which, by the end of the run, would leave you unable to open zips or extract anything from your pockets.

So, I needed an alternative to cut down on the number of puke glue packets that I'd be carrying with me over the four hours of the marathon. The answer, I was to discover after a quick scan of Instagram, was balls. Homemade energy balls to be precise.

My gel-replacement, special balls were in fact made of medjool dates, peanut butter, cocoa powder and desiccated coconut. Mashed together, squeezed into balls, chilled overnight in the fridge and then wrapped individually in silver foil. I had taken my balls on the last few long runs, neatly tucked into a (cough) ball bag that was attached around my waist and they had worked a treat. Alternating in half hourly intervals between gels and balls, I was able to cut down on the sickly gels and look forward to a tasty mini snack on the hour!

In fact, the alternation between gels and balls each half hour unconsciously meant that I saw the long runs, not in terms of multiple hours, but in 30-minute chunks. I would count down the minutes until I could reach for either of the two options, unwrap (or in the case of the gels, spend a few minutes struggling to open) my nutritional treat and enjoy the hit they would give me, before turning my mind to the next treat in around 27 minutes' time.

Setting off on my longest training run a week later, I therefore had a waist bag full of balls and a hydration vest with gels sticking out of assorted pockets. This was, without doubt, the most like a long-distance runner I had ever felt.

Back on the canal - albeit heading in the opposite direction to the previous week - I set off with the delicious prospect of a fortnight of tapering awaiting me as a reward for the effort I was about to put in. I had heard nothing but good things about tapering; reducing the time and mileage to ensure that I was at peak fitness; plenty of rest and, apparently, all you want to eat. As I locked on to a GPS signal, I was already mentally making my choice from the Domino's menu.

The run itself went well. The pace was reasonable and the juggling of gels and balls went to plan as I wound my around the Aldershot stretch of the Basingstoke Canal. What became immediately apparent as I did so, however, was that for all the northern stretch was beautiful, parts of the southern stretch were grim. Weaving its way between industrial parks and swapping majestic canalside oaks for barbed wire and car parks, my route may not have been as scenic, but it was just as rewarding. My legs felt strong and were carrying me with relative ease along the uneven paths, making me reflect at times on just how far I had come over the past four months.

The training plan that had at the start looked daunting, was actually paying dividends and, what's more, I actually

181

think that my mid-plan hip setback had helped me in the longer term. Forcing me to pay more attention to my weak core and spend more time on the floor - either in plank position or assorted bridges - the injury-induced advice from the physio had meant that I now had a stronger core that was not only supporting my hip better, but providing more structural integrity to the whole pelvic and lower back area, and making me feel generally stronger to boot.

By the time I returned home at the end of my longest training run I had clocked up 36.7km and - despite being understandably tired and sore - felt better than I had ever felt before.

There were two things I hadn't trained for, however.

The wall, and the maranoia.

Chapter 25 - Maranoia

No one tells you how horrendous the last two weeks before a marathon are, not because of the running - tapering, it turns out, is a joy - but because of the worry.

I had more or less completed my 16-week training programme, I had stayed free of serious injury, I had obtained a level of physical fitness never previously experienced and I had raised £2,500 for a charity to which I owed so much. My fear now was that the whole thing would come crashing down around me as a result of something completely out of my control, a cold.

While no one ever wants to catch a cold, I found myself facing a situation where I was going to have to do everything I possibly could to actively not catch a cold. At no other point in my life up to that moment had I faced a situation whereby I was going to have to go out of my way to avoid anyone who looked even vaguely like they were about to sneeze, blow their nose, cough or do anything that would see them sending germs in my direction.

Obviously, today, in the wake of coronavirus, such viral avoidance is commonplace and the addition to our lives of masks, social distancing, hand sanitiser and lockdowns, makes it easier for runners to steer clear of folks who are hell bent on sharing their bugs with other human beings. But in the pre-Covid times of 2019, the only masks in our household were the ones brought out at Halloween and social distancing in the workplace simply meant steering clear of Alan on one of his particularly bad BO days.

So while the fact that the tapering meant I could relax a bit in regards to training load, I found myself looking upon all those with whom I worked, lived and socialised with intense suspicion. Did Alison just blow her nose? Has Scott got a cough? Why's Sam looking so pale?

I also subsequently became my own ear, nose and throat consultant, more acutely aware than I have ever been of the three primary cold-related anatomical areas of concern. Was that a tickle in my throat? Is my nose running? Am I sounding a little horse?

The issue with trying to avoid a cold, however, is that the more you think about it, the more you convince yourself that you have the symptoms you are trying to desperately steer clear of. The fortnight before the marathon therefore saw me stocking up on entirely unnecessary cold and flu remedies in an effort to stave off the lurgy.

I also found myself Googling 'how to avoid a cold' and 'how to stop a cold before it starts' as well as a wealth of other scenarios that anyone scrutinising my search history would put down to the paranoid delusions of a Howard Hughes-style hypochondriac. My children, meanwhile, would return from school and run towards me for a cuddle, noses streaming. Every instinct in me wanted to hold them at arm's length or embrace them while wearing a hazmat suit and breathing apparatus, but instead I just had to hope that their friends hadn't passed them a particularly virulent strain of flu while playing tag in the playground.

It was tough.

The fear of not making it to the start of the Marathon was absolute. I don't think I had realised until that point exactly how important it actually was to me. Yes, there would be other races and even other opportunities to run the London Marathon in the future, but this event, at this time, for this charity and after all that the preceding year had entailed had come to represent a moment in my life at which I could, finally, move on from prostate cancer and get on with living.

This was so much more than just a marathon, it was a bright end to a rather dark and depressing chapter of my life. It was also something I had to do for all those people who had so generously sponsored me, for the stories they had shared with me and for the hope that the money I had raised represented for all those with prostate cancer in the future.

It would also bring an end to preceding all my Strava runs with a Fuck You Cancer (FYC) prefix and number, which had started as a bit of fun but had come to represent my whole recovery journey, from that first short run to the start line of the London Marathon. I had already worked out that the race itself would represent *FYC:164*, so I was living for the day when I could run without having to count the time that had passed.

All this self-administered pressure was why the thought of developing a cold or any kind of illness at this late stage was terrifying. It was also completely out of my control. I was pretty sure I could avoid straining my hamstring or rupturing my Achilles in the two remaining weeks, but I was far less confident about my ability to avoid invisible viruses.

An excess of nervous energy didn't make things any easier as the days ticked by. My dreams at night became marathon related, while I struggled to concentrate during the day, so preoccupied was I by trying to ascertain whether or not the tickly throat - that I probably didn't have - represented the first sign of a cold.

By the time the race weekend finally arrived, I was emotionally exhausted. Two weeks of self-absorbed worrying had proved far harder than 16 weeks of running. However, as I clocked up my last 10-minute pre-race leg warmer on the Saturday, laid out my Prostate Cancer UK running shirt, race number and other kit on the dining room floor, made sure my mobile phone charger was plugged in and checked the train times for the 15th time, I felt an overwhelming sense of relief.

I was fit, I was cold-free and I was ready for the 2019 Virgin Money London Marathon.

Chapter 26 - Raceday morning

S unday, April 28, 2019 began with a poo. Or at least an attempted poo. Having woken early and before the rest of the house in order to catch the first train into London, my immediate priority was to ensure that I had evacuated everything that needed evacuating, before leaving for the station. However, things did not go to plan in that department.

Having spent much of a restless night worrying about all that could go wrong en route to the start line - delayed trains, missed trains, underground issues, forgotten trainers, alien abductions and everything in between - the one thing I hadn't considered was what I would do if I wasn't able to poo before leaving home.

Without wanting to put you off your dinner - which I may already have done - a pre-run poo (as you may recall from the Fleet Half Marathon) has always been an essential part of my Sunday long run preparation. I had never previously, up to that point, had the misfortune of being caught short mid-run. The fear of being in the middle of nowhere - or worse, in the middle of somewhere very crowded - and urgently needing to find a toilet, toilet paper, soap, hand basin and towel had somehow meant that my body had naturally attuned to this and ensured that the rhythm of my bowel movements ran to an early morning beat. Or at least, it had done every Sunday up to that point.

So there I was, a little while later, stood on the London bound platform at Fleet Station, my uniquely numbered kit bag in hand, wondering if and where I was going to find somewhere to make the necessary deposit before being called to the start line at Blackheath. Yes, there would be toilets available at regular points along the course, but I didn't want to have to stop, queue and waste valuable time once the race was underway. Stopping also felt a little like cheating myself. I really wanted to see if I could run the whole course, without stopping, in under the four-hour milestone I had set myself. Detouring for a dump was not in the plan.

Attempting to put my downstairs dilemma to the back of my mind, I was joined on the journey by an increasing number of equally nervous marathon runners who boarded the train at various stops along the way. We exchanged knowing nods, but conversation was at a minimum as we all contemplated what lay ahead. As I glanced around the carriage, I wondered what the past 16 weeks had been like for each of my fellow runners. Had any of them picked up and overcome an injury? What training plan had they each followed? Who else had brought homemade energy balls with them? And who, if anyone, had been on a journey (to use an *X Factor* cliché) like my own.

◆◆◆

For the first time in months, I found myself thinking about Andrew, the chap with whom I had shared a ward after my prostatectomy. At a time when I had been scared and fearful of what lay ahead, he had brought calm reassurement and good humour, despite having gone through surgery for two different types of cancer himself. However, my morphine-filled brain hadn't thought to ask him for any contact details during our brief time together, so I had no idea at all how he was doing. Here I was, 14 months after surgery, on a train to run the London Marathon. As I glanced at the nervous, but clearly excited runners around me, I hoped that Andrew was currently doing something that he had dreamed of and living the life that he wanted, free from the worry of cancer. If anyone deserved to be doing so, it was him. Perhaps he was on a train to London himself right now, I hoped so.

Everyone on my train and on countless other trains destined for the Capital at that same moment had trained for months for this day. They had endured the wind, rain and freezing temperatures of the British winter. They had raised thousands for charities that each meant something special to them. They had bored everyone closest to them with marathon-related stories for the best part of a year and, judging by the amount of nail biting and leg shaking that was going on, none of them had managed a poo in the last two hours either. God, I hoped there were enough portaloos at Blackheath.

As I made my way through central London, via assorted tubes and trains - all the time becoming part of a bigger and bigger mass of nervous energy as the size of the crowd grew with every step - I felt for the first time like I was part of something really special. I'd run in races before, but I'd never been part of such a massive mass participation event. The staggering level of organisation to get 40,000 runners to the right place at the right time was evident from every piece of signage and every volunteer pointing the way. It was inspiring and reassuring in equal measure. My concerns about getting lost or ending up at the wrong start line were foundless.

Indeed, like a log (excuse the poo analogy) floating downstream, I was swept along with the masses and before I knew it, I had exited Maze Hill Station and was making my way to Greenwich Park and the red start line. Before arriving at the official starting area, however, I had been asked to meet the other Prostate Cancer UK runners at the Royal Observatory for the obligatory pre-race photograph. Following the signs, I made my way up the unexpectedly steep hill in the middle of Greenwich Park to the home of Greenwich Mean Time, where I was met by a young, energetic chap from the Charity's Marketing team, armed with a camera, who directed me to a spot overlooking the city of London.

All sporting the PCUK uniform of black t-shirt or vest - highlighted with blue, emblazoned with the name of the charity in bold white lettering and featuring its powerful 'man of men' figure on the back - we fleetingly gathered together, said cheese, exchanged best wishes and departed to make way for the next collection of charity runners to take their shot. I wished I could have had more time to stop, exchange stories and find out why this happy bunch of men and women had chosen to run for Prostate Cancer UK. The charity had chosen them all, based on the strength of their individual stories, so I suspected some of the men may, like me, have had prostate cancer, while others in the team had presumably lost fathers, uncles, brothers or grandfathers to the disease. Their stories may have been tinged with tragedy, but the enthusiasm and excitement on show that morning told a very different story; one of a group of people determined to do good on the hard work they had put in to reach this day, to honour the memories of those they'd lost or, like me, to thank the Charity for the support it had given them. It may have been brief, but the team photo was nevertheless uplifting and served to remind me once again of the journey I had been on and the many reasons I had to be grateful to be alive.

From there I made my way to the red start area and, after dropping off my bag at the correct, spectacularly well organised bag drop lorry, I spotted former *Blue Peter* presenter Radzi Chinyanganya chatting with members of a camera crew. Aware that he had long been a favourite of my children, I sidled over and secured a cheesy picture - momentarily taken back to the same time a year ago when I had been watching the energetic presenter from the comfort of my living room, in my dressing gown - before parting ways and finally making my way to the portaloo toilet queue.

Fully expecting the experience to be akin to Glastonbury, with the inside resembling something from a horror movie, I inched closer to the loos and was eventually surprised to find a more or less spotless cubicle, complete with air freshener and toilet paper. I took it as a good omen for the race to follow – perhaps it wasn't going to be as daunting as I had mentally built it up to be.

With that particular situation resolved, I could now focus on the matter in hand and, glancing up at the big screens that told us when to make our way to our respective start pens, I saw that the time had arrived. Just as at the Fleet Half Marathon, there were folks around me who were enthusiastically warming up, but they were few in number due to the fact that space in the park was limited. The majority, meanwhile, were walking aimlessly around looking nervous, like me.

Not really sure what the right thing to do was, I allowed myself a momentary warm up and stretch - the kind that neither warmed me up or adequately stretched anything - and then made my way to my starting pen on Blackheath Avenue.

Chapter 27 – FYC:164

S tanding patiently, jumping on the spot, stretching my hamstrings unnecessarily and waving as requested by a cameraman on a crane half a mile away, here I was waiting for the start of the 2019 Virgin Money London Marathon.

The moment seemed somewhat surreal. Was I really about to run 26.2 miles, from this familiar spot in East London to an even more familiar spot on The Mall, in the formidable shadow of Buckingham Palace? Well, yes, I was, whether I liked it or not. The moment had come and, as I shuffled forward with the masses, gradually breaking from a walk into a gentle jog - stepping over discarded clothes and checking for the 400th time that my watch had a GPS lock - I suddenly found myself running over the red timing mats that marked the start. Clicking the button on my watch that set it running, my immediate feeling was one of total relief.

The nerves disappeared instantly and, unlike previous race experiences, there was no stop-start congestion or shoulder barging, nor did I see any overly keen runners taking to the pavements and attempting an early sprint.

Although, having said that, there were vast numbers sprinting into hedges and bushes within the first kilometre, expelling the nervous wee they had convinced themselves they didn't need after presumably declining to partake of the portaloo experience. I now understood why the TV cameras never really covered much of the first couple of kilometres, and why the flora was rather unspectacular at this end of Greenwich Park.

Leaving the Park behind me, I was able to settle into a comfortable pace - around 5.35 a kilometre - and to take note of the East London surroundings that the route weaved its way through. Having watched the race on the TV for so many years, I was familiar with the legendary landmarks; Cutty Sark, Tower Bridge, Canary Wharf, the Victoria Embankment, Buckingham Palace and The Mall. That was where the TV presenters stationed themselves, jogging along with runners in assorted fancy dress costumes to ask them how they were getting on, commenting on the enthusiasm and determination of the masses and doing so while offering viewers a glimpse of some the Capital's most iconic sights. As I made my way through Blackheath, Charlton and Woolwich, there wasn't a single camera or former *Blue Peter* presenter in sight.

However, what it lacked in TV presence, it made up for with community spirit. The streets were lined with enthusiastic locals, young and old, cheering, holding signs, offering high five power-ups and, seemingly every few hundred yards, holding balcony parties with all genres of music blasting on to the street. Although it was too early in the run to need the psychological boost of the crowd, it brought a smile to everyone's faces and powered us along with a definite spring in our step. The less glamorous parts of our Capital may not have the best reputation but here, on Marathon day, the very best of human nature was on display. Strangers cheering on strangers, for no reason other than to show their support for the challenge they were undertaking.

It also became apparent early on that, the nearer to the pavement you were, the more likely the crowd was to shout your name - which was emblazoned proudly on the front of my shirt. This threw me at first and I pondered why these total strangers were shouting 'go on Tim,' in particular? Did I look like I was struggling? Did they know me? Why not the chap in front? Being British, I also found myself semi-shouting an appreciative; "thanks very much," which none of them heard as I was already 10 metres past them by the time I'd registered the shout and responded. Nevertheless, my ingrained politeness continued for at least the first 12-15 miles, after which tiredness began to take over and responding to anything verbal became one task too many. This must have been the same for 99 percent of the field, but despite this lack of runner feedback, the vocal by-name support continued and grew in both frequency and volume along the entire length of the course. It was wonderful.

Between miles six and seven, after doubling back through northern Greenwich, the route passes the first of its historic landmarks, the now-not-burned-down Cutty Sark. I hadn't realised it was approaching, however, until I'd rounded a corner and found it standing, ship-shape in front of me. Ever the tourist, I failed to take it in as I was too busy fumbling around with my phone trying, and almost spectacularly failing, to take a Sark-selfie while still running, something that I had promised myself I wouldn't do.

I have always poured scorn on those who feel inclined to pull out their phone for a self-indulgent selfie at any given moment, tut tutting as I pass, and judging them on their poor photographic composition. But there I was, mid-marathon, attempting to capture myself and a 19th Century ship, while simultaneously trying to maintain a consistent pace and not bump into any runners around me. I must have looked ridiculous and, had I fallen face first on to the road or sideways into the ship itself (only for my misfortune to have been captured on someone else's phone and uploaded to Twitter for the planet's amusement), I would have deserved it.

Having re-secured my phone and left the Cutty Sark behind me, I began to keep an eye out for my family as I hoped that - had their journey into town gone to plan - they would be watching out for me somewhere around mile eight. What I failed to take into account with them and discuss beforehand, however, was which side of the road they would be. For the best part of two miles I was therefore constantly scanning left and right to see if I could spot them. This soon became exhausting.

It turns out that the mental energy required to rapidly scan hundreds of faces is far greater than that needed to keep one's legs moving in the correct direction. So it was a relief, rounding a corner around mile eight, to spot my little cheer squad behind a pavement barrier, before they spotted me. I made my way over to them and, as they clocked me, a multitude of arms extended for a six-way hug. All also sporting Prostate Cancer UK t-shirts, waving inflatable PCUK clapper sticks and - thanks to my wife's encouragement I suspected - holding some 'Go Daddy' signs, it was amazing to see them. Alex told me I was apparently just behind Chris Evans – a real highlight for her, having been a fan of the bespectacled presenter since his *Don't Forget Your Toothbrush* days. We hugged, exchanged high-fives and parted ways - me to mile nine and they to a horrendous queue at the underground station, I definitely had the better deal.

From there, with a spring in my step, I made my way through Rotherhithe and Bermondsey, areas of the course again only briefly seen on the TV when the director is following the lead runners. Here, as elsewhere across the oft under-reported areas of the course, bands appeared from nowhere. Set up under bridges, in the middle of roundabouts or along pavements, bands of every kind supported us with pop, rock, kettle drums, jazz, big band, folk and countless other types of music. It was uplifting, inspiring and another totally unexpected part of the experience. I was particularly taken by the sight of an accordion player and troupe of morris dancers somewhere around Bermondsey Underground Station. Rarely has an age-old British tradition looked more out of place, but the jingle-belling group pulled it off with aplomb.

The next landmark to receive my unimpressive selfie treatment was Tower Bridge, rising majestically in front of us as my fellow runners and I turned on to Tower Bridge Road. Devoid of traffic, packed on either side by walls of spectators and, at mile 12, almost marking the halfway point of the race, it is perhaps the most familiar of all the London Marathon sights to those watching on TV. Running through its historic southerly tower and across its famous drawbridges, I was aware that I was grinning from ear to ear, so ready was I for my impromptu talking-while-running interview with the BBC's Gaby Logan. However, she was nowhere to be seen. Instead, a familiar ginger mop of hair appeared in front of me and, after overtaking, I glanced back to see that I had finally caught up with Chris Evans. Something to tell Alex when I saw her later anyway.

The high of Tower Bridge, however, was soon replaced with the disheartening sight of runners on the opposite side of The Highway, passing the 22-mile mark as I made my way past mile marker 13. Clearly considerably faster than I was, these serious runners had already conquered the Isle of Dogs and Canary Wharf and were probably no more than 25 minutes away from their medals and goody bags. One part of me was envious - and a very small part of me wanted to hop over the fence and join them - but I also took some comfort from the fact that I was getting more value out of my entrance fee. Yes, they may well finish somewhere within the two-hour window, but they'd have only got half the experience I was currently having. So, in a way, they may have beaten me on the stopwatch, but I was the real winner on the pound-per-minutes-run-ometer.

Heading into the Isle of Dogs, the crowds thinned slightly around Mudchute and Crossharbour, but as the course wound its way into the Canary Wharf financial district, the contrast in surroundings was marked. Miles 16-17 had made their way around the southernmost end of the Isle and through some of the most deprived areas of the country, where high unemployment and child poverty is an everyday reality. Miles 18-19, on the other hand, took us through one of the least deprived areas in the UK, complete with skyscrapers, multi-million-pound apartments, luxury cars and top-end restaurants.

The two areas literally occupy the same space, but the lives of their inhabitants are worlds apart. Unsure where the money was coming from to put food on the table in one street, versus unsure whether to choose fillet steak or lobster for a working lunch in the next. Running through both areas brought this home to me as the transition from one to the other was so sudden and so absolute. How is this possible in modern day London?

The friendliness of the people, however, was consistent. The cheers and support from the locals across the whole Isle of Dogs - rich and poor - was selfless and uplifting. I found this to be one of the toughest parts of the course as I was running in the opposite direction to my final destination and beginning to feel the long run bite as the mileage hit the late teens, so I was once again grateful for the crowd support. Mind you, my fingers were also a sticky mess of gel juice and energy balls by this point, which didn't help matters.

The finger issue was partly eased a short while later, however, as some friends waiting patiently near One Canada Square hollered in my direction. I rushed over, gave them the obligatory hug and no doubt left them pondering over their washing a few days later as to where the wholly unpleasant sticky residue on the back of their jumpers had come from.

After that point, the going began to get tougher.

I had read about the infamous wall - that moment in the marathon where things transition from being hard to being really, "fuck me, this is impossible," hard - but I had never experienced anything like that on any of my training runs, so naively assumed that the extra 45 minutes or so on top of my longest training run couldn't be that hard. How wrong I was.

It was around Mile 21 - somewhere near Limehouse - that my encounter with the wall began. My legs became inexplicably heavy and I could feel my pace slow. Like running through treacle, everything suddenly seemed to require more effort. For the first time in the race, I reached for one of the tubs of jelly babies that kind spectators seemed to be offering every few hundred yards, in the hope that a sugar hit might translate into more energy. It didn't work.

I really didn't want to, but I felt that I had to stop and stretch out my legs a little, before cramp set in or they just stopped working altogether. So, pulling over to the side of the course for a minute or so, I leant against a railing, in front of complete strangers, to stretch my calves, hamstrings and quads. Incredibly, I felt hands patting me on the back and heard kind words of encouragement.

"You can do it mate, you've come so far, not long now."

"You've got this. Dig deep mate."

"Here you go, have a Jelly Baby."

It was another example of the kindness that had been demonstrated by strangers along the whole length of the course. I had seen it being given to others who, like me, had needed to take a moment to sort out their misbehaving legs and on each occasion it served to remind me of the inherent good that is in most people. In a world where so much news is dominated by the very worst of humanity, a marathon, it transpires, is a brilliant place to come to see some of the best.

Now fully stretched, sugared up and back on the road, my legs still felt like they belonged to a large African elephant, but I pushed on regardless and with a renewed determination to see out the last five miles as best as I possibly could.

A short while later, just as the Jelly Baby sugar hit was wearing off, I spotted my cheer squad once again. This time positioned in perfect eye shot and just before the course made its way towards the Victoria Embankment, I ran - or rather sidled - over to them and was a little taken aback to see a few teary eyes and concerned faces. Did I really look that bad? Evidently so. The embraces were fierce, I felt a lump in my throat and all I managed to mutter was a rather emotional; "It's so hard," before I left them and returned my focus to seeing out the pain and completing the last few miles. As a side note, the race photos from this period of the race made me realise why my family looked so concerned. Far from looking like an athlete at the peak of his physical fitness, all the colour had drained out of my face, leaving me looking like John Major in shorts. It wasn't a pretty sight.

Ahead, I knew that the Victoria Embankment, London Eye, Parliament Square and then Buckingham Palace were all that stood between me and my finisher's medal. However, the way I was feeling, I knew that those last two miles were going to feel like a marathon in themselves. I also had to get there first and the darkness of the Blackfriars Underpass lay before me, almost teasing me by denying me the sight of the Thames and the riverside landmarks I knew so well from my years of working in the Capital.

However, in perhaps the most inspired piece of marketing I have ever seen, the sportswear brand New Balance had set up a raucous cheer squad and band at the foot of the tough uphill exit from the underpass. Complete with drumming band, whoops and whistles, it provided the drive that every runner who passed it needed at that moment in time. From a place of self-absorbed fear and pain, I found that the deafening noise and beat of the drums made me momentarily forget the discomfort and remember the occasion. Having passed the band, climbed up and out of the underpass, I was on the Embankment, with Waterloo Bridge ahead of me and the promise of the finish tantalisingly close.

Those last two miles were two of the strangest I have ever run. Physically I was exhausted, in pain and probably looking the worst I had ever looked in a pair of shorts, but emotionally I was absolutely buzzing. Knowing that I had less than 15 minutes left to run, that each of the landmarks I was now passing - Cleopatra's Needle, the London Eye, the spot where I used to have lunch with Keith (the lifelong friend who, you may recall, challenged me to my first ever 10K race) - all meant that my head was spinning with a heady mix of conflicting endorphins.

Midway along the Embankment, amidst the pandemonium of noise from spectators, I heard someone screaming "Tiiiiiiiiiiiiim" and glanced to my left to briefly catch a glimpse of a friend waving me on with spectacular energy. In my befuddled state, however, it took about 200 metres of forward momentum for my eyes to transfer the data to my brain and then enable my arm to wave a response. I made a mental note to thank her when I next saw her and powered on.

Into Parliament Square, along Birdcage Walk next to St James' Park, I could sense those around me picking up the pace a little in order to end with a flourish. My legs weren't having any of that, however, and were now carrying me along at an auto-pilot pace that was entirely out of my control. Rounding the top of St James' Park, the welcome sight of Buckingham Palace greeted me. This was it. I'd reached the end of the London Marathon and as I turned onto The Mall, my back now to the Palace, the lump in my throat returned.

All that now stood between me and the completion of a 16-month personal challenge were a few hundred yards of The Mall's distinctive red-tarmaced carpet. Fighting back the tears, I thought briefly of all that had happened over that time, of the friends, family, colleagues and strangers who had sponsored me and of how grateful I was to be here, completing this race, on this day, alive and healthy.

As I neared the finish line, I could see 4.19.55 on the timing clocks above the four gateways. I hadn't managed to finish in under four hours, but I couldn't have cared less. I was going to finish and, running over the timing mats, I pressed stop on my watch to officially bring my London Marathon to a close. I had run 26.2 miles for the first time in my life and with a medal soon thereafter placed around my neck, I had the bling to prove it.

Standing for a few moments amongst the bustle of exhausted but elated runners, I pulled out my phone for another indulgent selfie, but opted instead to ask a fellow finisher to take a photo for me. He did, and I took one of him in return, before we shook hands, congratulated each other once again and went our separate ways. I had no idea what kind of a journey he had been on to reach that point, but our brief encounter summed up the joyfulness and positivity of every aspect of the preceding four hours, 20 minutes and one second. I was utterly exhausted, but I had loved every mile - with the possible exception of miles 20-24 - and, as I made my way to collect my goody bag and obligatory foil sheet, I knew that I'd do it all again in a heartbeat.

Chapter 28 - The post-race rub down

A short while later, I made my way - wrapped in a foil blanket, my medal proudly hanging around my neck – past Nelson's Column to St Martin-in-the-Fields, a spectacular church in the north east corner of Trafalgar Square.

Here, I finally met up with my cheer squad, who grabbed me for cuddles, despite the fact that I was the sweatiest and smelliest I had ever been. There were a few tears, lots of 'how are yous?' and a fair bit of medal manhandling, after which, with my legs now complaining bitterly that I was still making them stand, we all made our way to the Prostate Cancer UK post-race party.

Held in the Crypt, where the lift was frustratingly out of order, my family made their way down the spiraling stairs, while I followed slowly behind. Awaiting us below ground were the smiling faces of the PCUK team, pointing my family to the refreshments and me to the welcoming hands of a complimentary sports masseuse.

After exchanging brief pleasantries, I hopped up onto the bench and let the smiling miracle man do his thing. Clearly experienced in the needs of post-marathon amateurs, my legs were expertly handled over the following 15 minutes as they enjoyed the lower limb equivalent of a trip to *The Repair Shop*. Indeed, had this been an episode of the popular BBC One show, I would have arrived, talking nostalgically about my legs' long and emotional back story, after which the personable leg expert would intricately explain how knackered they were and how a lengthy massage would be required before handing them back to their overjoyed owner.

Needless to say, *The Repair Shop* man almost reduced me to tears, so grateful were my legs at the care and attention that had been shown to them. After thanking the masseuse, I made my way to the refreshment area, where PCUK had laid on a hearty lunch for all its runners and their family members. It was an incredible and unexpected gesture that only served to reaffirm for me how brilliant this life-saving charity is.

Taking a moment before piling into an enormous plate of spaghetti bolognese, I took myself and a bag of clean clothes to the nearest toilet cubicle, where I changed and spent a few minutes updating my Strava record for the race.

Sat there, on a toilet in the middle of central London, I added the title *FYC 164: Virgin Money London Marathon* and felt an overwhelming sense of relief that I would never, I hoped, have to type those three prefixed letters again. Right then, however, I was rather disappointed to also see that my GPS signal had dropped in and out around Canary Wharf's various underpasses to leave my route map with far too many straight lines. Furthermore, my obsession with Strava was clearly getting out of hand; what was I doing there in the toilet when my family and fellow runners were outside enjoying lunch? I turned my phone off and headed for the food.

Over lunch I chatted the race through with my family, answered the children's continuous flow of questions as best I could and savoured the protein-packed food that my muscles were craving. As I did so, other members of the PCUK team continued to arrive, all looking exhausted, but all smiling. Before long, the large dining room was packed with the buzz of family groups enjoying time together and celebrating the achievement of the individuals they had come to support. Collectively, however, the room represented hundreds of thousands of pounds of fundraising achievement, all of which would go towards helping the early diagnosis of prostate cancer and, ultimately, a cure for a disease that currently impacts the lives of one in eight men in the UK.

While running a marathon can be seen as an in inherently selfish activity - with countless hours spent away from family and even more spent boring those around you with stories of sore joints and aching muscles - it is also perhaps the biggest of all team events, with 40,000 individuals coming together in London once a year to change the lives of millions in need across the UK. This collective effort over the course of one day each year makes a difference to so many others, allowing charities to keep their doors open, funding vital research projects and opening opportunities up to people for whom they would otherwise be closed. Pondering this thought, while glancing around the room and demolishing another slice of garlic bread, was incredibly humbling.

Charities like Prostate Cancer UK and that for which I work can be almost entirely dependent on voluntary income from fundraising. Many raise additional income through merchandise sales, trust or grant funding, but the majority of charities in the UK rely on the runners, cyclists, cake bakers, coffee sale hosts, raffle ticket sellers and payroll donors amongst us to keep their doors open.

Thankfully, as was evident in that large room - which smelt not unpleasantly of both bolognese sauce and sweaty feet - the UK is the second most charitable nation on the planet, behind the United States. Indeed, according to NPT UK, 60 percent of Britons give each year, with the average person donating a total of £44 every 12 months.

However, as the coronavirus pandemic has proven, this dependence on voluntary income can prove costly when fundraising events, like marathons, are cancelled or postponed. At the height of the Covid-19 crisis in 2020, Nottingham Trent University revealed that 80 percent of charities had reported a negative impact on their ability to deliver services, with one in 10 fearing closure due to dire financial circumstances.

Although brought about by an unforeseen and unprecedented set of circumstances, this devastating impact on the third sector has only served to highlight its fragility and the importance, for us all, of doing what we can to support the charities that mean something to us. For some that may well mean running a marathon sometime in the future, for others it could be a cycle race, a mountain climb, a coffee morning or a car boot sale. While for many it will mean choosing to give personally and regularly to an organisation they care about.

For me, I will forever support Prostate Cancer UK in any way I can and, as I left St Martin-in-the-Fields that April afternoon in 2019, with my family in tow, I did so with a sense of personal accomplishment, both for the race I had just run and the contribution my supporters had hopefully made to a thoroughly deserving cause.

Taking the bus over Westminster Bridge en route to Waterloo Station soon after, we glanced down at the Victoria Embankment to see a thinning number of runners still on the course, over six hours into the race. Many were clearly struggling, but they were fighting on, sporting the colourful shirts of the charities they cared about, determined to get to the end.

Whether keeping in touch with the elite runners, or bringing up the rear, I felt a kinship with every runner who had donned trainers that morning to take on the 26.2 miles of the Capital. Indeed, I felt a kinship with every runner who had ever run the Marathon up to that point, helping it to raise over £1bn for good causes since its foundation in 1981.

My friends, family and colleagues - together with the generosity of strangers - had helped to turn my personal struggle into an opportunity to fund life-changing support for someone who would be facing prostate cancer in the future and, as I found a spot on the floor of the packed train carriage home, my children in my arms, I fell asleep thinking how lucky I was.

Epilogue

In the immediate few days after the Marathon the smile barely left my face, apart from every time I attempted to walk up or down stairs. No one had told me how bad the DOMS was going to be and none of my training runs had prepared me for the superhuman challenge of simply getting from one floor of my house to the next. Taking a good week to dissipate, my legs felt like they were punishing me for putting them through the 26.2 miles, and no amount of hot baths or massage would make them go easy on me either.

But it was a short-lived hardship that I was more than happy to put up with. I had completed what I had set out to do and raised over £2,500 for Prostate Cancer UK. I was proud of that achievement and hopeful that the money would go some way to helping someone else to come to terms with prostate cancer. The charity had helped me greatly and running for them was something I felt honoured and proud to do. The shirt also remains one of my regular running favourites, although sadly few people around my local roads and trails tend to shout my name when I'm wearing it.

The Marathon came 14 months after my radical prostatectomy and 16 months after my diagnosis. At that time I was having repeat PSA tests every three months to ensure that the cancer had not returned, but today those tests have become six monthly and I remain in remission, or as I prefer to think of it, cancer free.

From the moment I was diagnosed, running helped me to come to terms with my cancer, to prepare for my treatment and recover from it. The physical and mental benefits were intrinsically linked throughout, symbiotically working together to give me the strength I needed in my body and mind to come to terms with the fact that I was an anomaly in the prostate cancer gene pool. For my age, race and family history, I was a 10,000-to-one rank outsider, but lacing up my trainers and hitting the streets distracted me from dwelling on my misfortune. Instead, it gave me a focus and an ability to control my physical wellbeing in the face of one small cancerous part over which I had no control. Mentally, meanwhile, it helped me through the endless days of waiting, pulling me off the sofa and out of my self-absorbed sorrow; it helped me to work through my worries, with a clarity of thought that was so much easier to find when running at speed along the canal towpath on a cold winter morning.

Time outdoors, walking and then running - together with the care and love of my wife and children - helped me through the hard weeks and months of recovery after surgery. The physical scars healed quicker than the mental ones, but training for the London Marathon provided the vehicle I needed to put prostate cancer behind me. I knew from the moment I submitted the application form that the

213

months of hard work would provide the perfect distraction from the challenging - but I hoped short term - lifestyle implications that result from prostate cancer surgery. And so it proved to be, on both fronts.

I threw myself into the Marathon, physically, emotionally and in my entirety, not because I was trying to escape real life, but because it felt like the right thing to do. The result was that, while I admittedly became slightly obsessed and probably bored those around me to tears, I felt myself getting physically and mentally stronger as the weeks passed. My running endurance improved and, with it, the periods of time I spent worrying or wallowing became fewer and less intense.

To that end, I am living proof that the link between physical activity and mental wellbeing is a real and powerful one. When first diagnosed, I turned to running rather than alcohol to deal with the intense anxiety and stress of a situation that was entirely out of my control. It also gave me a means by which I could expel my anger at the world in a constructive way, taking it out on the trails rather than anyone who would otherwise have been on the receiving end of my intense grumpiness.

Today, the Marathon may well be behind me, but I have taken so much from it into my life. I am running more regularly now in my 40s than at any previous point in my life and running remains central to both my physical and mental wellbeing.

As was the case for many, running during the coronavirus pandemic proved once again to be an elixir to Covid-19's stresses and strains. But global pandemics aside, it remains the familiar vehicle to which I turn whenever I feel anxious or stressed with everyday life, including the repeat PSA tests that still cast a deep shadow every six months.

My arsenal of anxiety-busting running tools has, however, been bolstered by the addition of running club membership since completing the marathon. Having always previously run solo, I joined my local running club in the wake of London and soon discovered exactly why so many remain committed members into their 70s. The camaraderie and shared drive that comes from running regularly with others is palpable and adds an entirely new dimension to the running experience. I'd recommend it to anyone.

On my own, meanwhile, I have found myself increasingly drawn to trail running and the child-like adventure of discovering paths and routes through unexplored forests and new patches of countryside. Searching out the trails less trodden has taken me away from the hustle and bustle of life, allowing me to pack away reality in exchange for often blissful silence. Indeed, there is something almost ethereal about running along a trail only to stop in your tracks when you round the corner to find yourself face to face with a roe deer. It is as far from a run through city streets as can be, yet the sport is the same.

This is the magic of running. It is one of only a handful of pastimes that can be done anywhere, anytime, taking its devotees to new places, offering new experiences and rewarding them with improved physical and mental health.

Today I am pleased to say that, although tested on occasion - global pandemics, home schooling, PSA tests and being a fan of Fulham Football Club - my mental health is in a good place. Of course, I know that I am lucky to have had my cancer caught at a treatable stage and the thought of the alternative still makes me feel sick, but I believe the twin experiences of cancer and the London Marathon have made me mentally stronger and able to cope better with the ups and downs of life.

I remain a supporter and ambassador of Prostate Cancer UK - who you have yourself supported by buying this book - and I am doing whatever I can to persuade men in their 40s to get their PSA levels checked. The fact that prostate cancer kills more men in the UK than any other form of cancer is a shocking fact that doesn't need to be. If more men knew their PSA level, from their 40s, they would be able to monitor it over time and crucially detect irregular rises early. And if prostate cancer can be detected early, survival chances go through the roof. It is not rocket science, thankfully, so I'm going to shout it from the roof tops.

I am also committed to doing what I can to champion men's health in general and to help break down the stigma and machismo that holds so many men back from seeking help when they need it, with both their physical and mental health. Fear, anxiety and even shame are understandable feelings for men when confronted with a personal health scare, but the impact of ignoring the issue can often be far more dangerous than the issue itself. So, if there's one thing I'd like every man reading this book to take away, it's the importance of confronting those things that are weighing heavy on your mind, seeking help and working your way through whatever comes next. Life is far too precious to throw it away for the sake of pride or embarrassment.

In fact, if you own a prostate, are reading this and are over 40, I want you to pledge to book yourself in for a PSA test before your next birthday. Being proactive with all aspects of your health can only ever be a good thing and, when it comes to prostate cancer, it could end up saving your life, which brings me nicely on to the National Health Service.

I am hopeful that I will remain cancer free on my next birthday, but if I hadn't attended my free NHS health check aged 40, I wouldn't be. Indeed, if I had ignored the appointment card that fell through my letterbox, I would probably now be carrying an incurable tumour that would have shortened my life significantly, leaving my children without their dad and my wife without a husband. So, as well as campaigning to raise awareness of prostate cancer amongst younger men, I will always defend the honour of the NHS and encourage everyone who is invited to a free health check to attend it. We are so fortunate to live in a country with a free to access healthcare system that proactively reaches out to help us. We need to cherish it, look after it and make a point of thanking all those who work in it. I am sure those of you reading this who don't have a free to access healthcare system would agree.

So, what next?

Running has undoubtedly been the wonder drug that has picked me up and carried me through the past few years, it is the comfort blanket I have come to depend upon and the trusted friend I routinely turn to when I need to vent my frustrations or take my mind off my troubles. I am grateful to it and, providing I can steer clear of injuries, I want to spend the rest of my life in trainers, seeing where my running adventures take me. I recommend you do the same.

Take care, keep running and I'll see you on the trails.

Acknowledgements

If I hadn't been diagnosed with prostate cancer in 2017, I would not have run the 2019 London Marathon and I would never have written this book. I would also probably now be carrying around an incurable tumour, so my first note of thanks has to go to the NHS for saving my life. It is an institution that we are blessed to have in the UK and one that I hope is preserved for generations to come.

My thanks also to Prostate Cancer UK for providing me with such fantastic advice and information. An understanding voice at the end of the phone when my mind was swimming with anxiety was exactly what I needed and I will forever be indebted to you.

To all those who donated towards my London Marathon challenge and who shared your own cancer stories with me, I remain as touched by your generosity and kindness today as I was back then. And to all those runners I've met on the roads and trails over the years - whether running together or just through a smile as we passed - thank you for your kinship. Ours is a sport of individual challenges, but one that is united through shared obsession and camaraderie.

Thanks also to my parents, brothers and assorted other familial folks across the country for your kind words and support over a tough year. I may not always have listened, or appeared appreciative, but knowing you're behind me has always given me great strength.

Finally, to my incredible family. Alex, William and Molly, thank you for putting up with my self-indulgence, allowing me to disappear for hours on end and for always being there when I need you. I love you more than you can ever know.

One last request

If you've enjoyed *The Running Drug*, I would be very grateful if you could leave a review on Amazon. Your words are far more important than mine as they help other readers to decide whether the book is right for them. Thank you again for reading.

Fleet, Hampshire, England
August 2021

Printed in Great Britain
by Amazon

75323988R00137